SECRET SHAKESPEARE'S

adventures
of
freeman jones

♈

EDited & DEliVEREd

by

Michael Brame & Galina Popova

ADONIS
EDITIONS

ADONIS EDITIONS

info@adonis-editions.com
http://www.adonis-editions.com

to
Roxanne Brame
dEDicatED

So sweet a thing
It is to sigh upon the rack of love.
The Two Gentlemen of Verona.

Library of Congress Control No. 2003116053

Manufactured in the United States of America

ISBN 0-9720385-1-5 (hard cover)
ISBN 0-9720385-3-1 (soft cover)

LETTER TO LOVERS OF LOFTY LITERATURE
by Way of Introducing Secret Shakespeare

Esteemed Lovers, Verifiable or Edifiable,

Have you ever wondered how a novel by Shakespeare would have turned out, had he written one? If so, here is your answer; if not, a pleasant surprise is in store, for the novel that graces your presence was indeed written by the man lurking behind the celebrated *Shakespeare* pseudonym. It was published in 1573, embedded within the context of a much larger anonymous work entitled *A Hundreth Sundrie Flowres,* hereafter referred to as *Flowers.* As early as 1926, B.M. Ward had attributed some of the poetry of *Flowers* to Edward de Vere, 17th Earl of Oxford. In the first installment of our trilogy, *Shakespeare's Fingerprints,* we adduced evidence confirming the stronger claim that all of *Flowers* was the creation of Oxford. Some of the linguistic evidence supporting Shakespeare-Oxford's creative authority, though by no means all, is recapitulated in the essay following this our modern spelling edition of the novel, including new arguments bearing out our earlier claims.

The *Freeman Jones* novel is the first offering in our projected *Secret Shakespeare Series.* Throughout the compass of this series we part company with orthodox scholars who consistently fail to take cognizance of Oxford's pseudonyms and anonyms appearing within a lavish variety of works published during the Golden Age of English literature, an unfortunate failure whose consequences include, among others, a tragic inability to recognize Shakespeare's genius as a novelist.

The contents of *Flowers* is traditionally attributed to the soldier-poet George Gascoigne, but the preponderance of evidence shows that the real-life Gascoigne was just one among those Elizabethan functionaries who lent names to

Oxford's lifetime program of elevating English to a status equaling, if not surpassing, that already achieved on the continent by the vernacular literatures of French, Italian, and Spanish authors. In fact, Oxford's agenda in no small part dovetailed with, and was at least in part sponsored by, the Tudor regime, whose *de facto* head, interestingly, was none other than Oxford's father-in-law, William Cecil, Lord High Treasurer to the Crown.

By recognizing the author of *Flowers* to be the very man who wrote under the *Shakespeare* pseudonym, we join hands with an emerging body of scholars and lovers from all walks of life—lawyers, actors, novelists, reporters, and others—who acknowledge the Earl of Oxford to be the supreme literary master who penned the famous plays and the luminous sonnets.

In this first offering of our projected series, we prosecute our goal of shedding light on Oxford's covert works so that they may be made available to a wider segment of our loving populace—to those who are lovers of lofty literature as also to those who have a desire to cultivate their literary taste and eschew, or perhaps recover from, the plague of 'bestsellerdom' with its attendant untruth in packaging.

In addition to the reasons for attributing the Freeman Jones novel to Oxford-Shakespeare, laid out in the essay following the text proper, additional arguments will be found in the second installment of our fingerprint trilogy, *Never and For Ever,* wherein we dwell on the important topic of Shakespeare as a novelist in more detail.

The novel reprinted here made its debut within the framework of *Flowers* as *The Adventures Passed by F.I.* From the original text we learn that the initials *F.I.* were intended as an abbreviation for the name *Freeman Jones,* the second letter of *F.I.* in the original being an Elizabethan precursor to our modern orthographic *J.* That this unexpurgated version of Secret Shakespeare's novel caused unease among some segments of the nobility and was destined for censorship is suggested by a partially sanitized revision appearing later under a new title, whose setting is shifted from England to Italy, the initials *F.J.* and name *Freeman Jones* suppressed, and the author's bold allusions partially masked by substitution of new Italian names, including *Ferdinando Jeronimi* and *Leonora* for the novel's protagonist and mistress, respectively. The author's identity was further obscured by adoption of the pseudonym *George Gascoigne* as a substitute for the Latin "posy" *Meritum petere grave,* placed on the original title page of 1573, a facsimile of which is provided on page 186 of the authorship essay following the text of the novel.

Why would the author want to translate the original setting of his novel from his native island to a foreign land? One possible answer can be found in what many scholars have long suspected, that the original novel was in no small part a reflection of events in the author's personal life. This being so, the characters of the first edition of the novel were identifiable with some of Oxford's contemporaries. Since the characters were drawn from the English nobility, including noblemen, noblewomen, and possibly the Queen herself, the novel must have created considerable unease within the realm. Couple the author's bold references with his scandalous inclusion of adultery, cuckoldry, and what some have interpreted as rape, and we suspect that there was no little pressure exerted by powerful Elizabethans to have *Flowers* called in and burned by the authorities.

Several orthodox scholars have awarded the novel presented here pride of place as our first English novel. Among such claimants is found the indefatigable Hyder Rollins, who advanced this controversial thesis as early as 1934. Although his position is disputable, the early date of the novel is sufficient warrant and justification for an Oxfordian edition accessible to readers interested in truth in packaging. That the novel, moreover, is one of Oxford's earliest and finest provides our personal motivation as editors to make it available as the first in our projected series.

Experience teaching and analyzing Elizabethan literature at the university level has taught us that students, unlike academicians, can and do quickly grasp and appreciate that this novel was the work of the genius many of us know by the name of *William Shakespeare*. As interest in the genuine genius continues to grow, your editors consider the present an opportune time to begin reclaiming our heritage, helping to make Oxford-Shakespeare's authorship of novels more generally recognizable and the novels themselves available to those lovers who already appreciate the transcendent sonnets and the glorious plays.

Anyone expecting to find here a "modern" novel will be disappointed. What one does encounter is far better, a work reminiscent of Shakespeare's plays and poetry, or in other words one replete with intelligence, depth of understanding and good taste, even in the context of his ubiquitous wanton wordplay, all of which is fortified by a most remarkable subtlety inspired by a brilliant intellect. Should readers devote the requisite time the novel deserves, they may also discover a genius framed in no small degree by what the author himself terms *aliquid salis*. The fact that the novel's characters are modeled after real-life Elizabethans should render their motions in the novel all the more engaging to the modern reader.

From our offices at the University of Washington in the beautiful Pacific Northwest on this 12th day of proud-pied April 2003, we remain your editors and would-be deliverers,

Michael Brame and Galina Popova.

Acknowledgement: Again we are grateful to Prof. Sharon Hargus and to Kayleen Doornbos for their discerning comments.

A discourse of the adventures
passed by Master F.J.

H. VV. to the Reader.

In August last-passed, my familiar friend Master G.T. bestowed upon me the reading of a written book, wherein he had collected divers discourses and verses, invented upon sundry occasions by sundry gentlemen, in mine opinion right commendable for their capacity. And here withal my said friend charged me that I should use them only for mine own particular commodity and eftsoons[†] safely deliver the original copy to him again, wherein I must confess myself but half a merchant, for the copy unto him I have safely redelivered. But the work—for I thought it worthy to be published—I have entreated my friend A.B. to imprint, as one that thought better to please a number by common commodity than to feed the humor of any private person by needless singularity.

This I have adventured for thy contentation,[†] learned reader, and further have presumed of myself to christen it by the name of *A Hundred Sundry Flowers,* in which poetical posy are set forth many trifling fantasies, humoral passions, and strange affects of a lover. And therein although the wiser sort would turn over the leaf as a thing altogether fruitless, yet I myself have reaped this commodity to sit and smile at the fond devices of such as have enchained themselves in the golden fetters of fantasy, and having bewrayed[†] themselves to the whole world, do yet conjecture that they walk unseen in a net.

[†]*eftsoons*. soon after, presently.
[†]*contentation*. pleasure, satisfaction.
[†]*bewrayed*. revealed

Some other things you may also find in this book, which are as void of vanity as the first are lame for government. And I must confess that—what to laugh at the one and what to learn by the other—I have contrary to the charge of my said friend G.T. procured for these trifles this day of publication, whereat if the authors only repine[†] and the number of other learned minds be thankful, I may then boast to have gained a bushel of good will in exchange for one pint of peevish choler. But if it fall out contrary to expectation that the readers' judgments agree not with mine opinion in their commendations, I may then—unless their courtesies supply my want of discretion—with loss of some labor account also the loss of my familiar friends, in doubt whereof I cover all our names and refer you to the well-written letter of my friend G.T. next following, whereby you may more at large consider of these occasions. And so I commend the praise of other men's travails together with the pardon of mine own rashness unto the well-willing minds of discrete readers. From my lodging near the Strand the twentieth of January 1572.

H.W.

The letter of G.T. to his very[†] friend
H.W. concerning this work.

Remembering the late conference passed between us in my lodging and how you seemed to esteem some pamphlets which I did there show unto you far above their worth in skill, I did straightway conclude the same your judgment to proceed of two especial causes: one—and principal—the steadfast good will which you have ever hitherto sithens[†]

[†]*repine.* complain, fret.
[†]*very.* one of many plausible puns on the author's family name *Vere* appearing throughout the novel, as those unnoted on the previous page.
[†]*sithens.* since.

our first familiarity borne towards me, another—of no less weight—the exceeding zeal and favor that you bear to good letters, the which, I agree with you, do no less bloom and appear in pleasant ditties or compendious sonnets devised by green youthful capacities than they do fruitfully flourish unto perfection in the riper works of grave and gray-haired writers. For as in the last the younger sort may make a mirror of perfect life, so in the first the most frosty bearded philosopher may take just occasion of honest recreation, not altogether without wholesome lessons, tending to the reformation of manners. For who doubteth but that poets in their most feigned fables and imaginations have metaphorically set forth unto us the right rewards of virtues and the due punishments for vices?

Marry, indeed I may not compare pamphlets unto poems, neither yet may justly advant[†] for our native countrymen that they have in their verses hitherto—translations excepted—delivered unto us any such notable volume as have been by poets of antiquity left unto the posterity. And the more pity that amongst so many toward wits no one hath been hitherto encouraged to follow the trace of that worthy and famous knight Sir Geoffrey Chaucer, and after many pretty devices spent in youth for the obtaining a worthless victory might consume and consummate his age in describing the right pathway to perfect felicity with the due preservation of the same, the which although some may judge overgrave a subject to be handled in style metrical, yet for that I have found in the verses of eloquent Latinists, learned Greeks, and pleasant Italians, sundry directions whereby a man may be guided toward th'attaining of that unspeakable treasure.

[†]*advant.* boast.

I have thus far lamented that our countrymen have chosen rather to win a passover praise[†] by the wanton penning[†] of a few loving lays[†] than to gain immortal fame by the clerkly handling of so profitable a theme. For if quickness of invention, proper vocables, apt epithets, and store of monosyllables may help a pleasant brain to be crowned with laurel, I doubt not but both our countrymen and country language might be enthronized[†] among the old foreleaders unto the Mount Helicon.[†]

But now let me return to my first purpose, for I have wandered somewhat beside the path, and yet not clean out of the way. I have thought good, I say,[†] to present you with this written book wherein you shall find a number of sonnets, lays, letters, ballads, rondelets, verlays,[†] and verses, the works of your friend and mine, Master F.J., and divers others, the which when I had with long travail confusedly gathered together, I thought it then *opere precium*[†] to reduce them into some good order, the which I have done according to my barren skill in this written book, commending it unto you to read and to peruse. And desiring you, as I only do adventure, thus to participate the sight thereof unto your former good will, even so that you will by no means make the same common, but after your own recreation

---

[†]*passover praise*. praise easily passed over.
[†]*penning*. pun on the pudendum, as expounded in the appended essay.
[†]*lays*. songs; what the author penned in a bawdy sense.
[†]*enthronized*. enthroned.
[†]*Helicon*. author's Greek "*hill where poets feign that the Muses sleep*", in response to which Gabriel Harvey emended "sleep" as "wake".
[†]*I say*. interpolation typical of Shakespeare:

> Sonnet 43:   How would, *I say*, mine eyes be blessèd made.
> Sonnet 71:   O if, *I say*, you look upon this verse,

[†]*verlays*. possible play on the lays of Vere, despite Chaucer's 'balades, roundels, virelayes' in *The Legend of Good Women*, the latter noted in Pigman [2000: 559].
[†]*opere precium*. worthwhile work.

taken therein that you will safely redeliver unto me the original copy. For otherwise I shall not only provoke all the authors to be offended with me, but farther shall lease the opportunity of a greater matter, half and more granted unto me already by the willing consent of one of them.

And to be plain with you my friend, he hath written— which as far as I can learn did never yet come to the reading or perusing of any man but himself—two notable works, the one called *The Sundry Lots of Love*, the other of his own invention entitled *The Climbing of An Eagle's Nest*. These things, and especially the latter, doth seem by the name to be a work worthy the reading. And the rather I judge so because his fantasy is so occupied in the same as that contrary to his wonted use, he hath hitherto withheld it from sight of any his familiars. Until it be finished you may guess him by his Nature.[†] And therefore I require your secrecy herein, lest if he hear the contrary, we shall not be able by any means to procure these other at his hands. So fare you well from my chamber this tenth of August 1572.[†]

Yours or not his own.
G. T.

When I had with no small entreaty obtained of Master F.J. and sundry other toward young gentlemen the sundry copies of these sundry matters, then as well for that the number of them was great as also for that I found none of them so barren but that, in my judgment, had in it *aliquid salis*,[†] and especially being considered by the very proper

---

[†]*Nature.* apparent clue to the author's identity, for which see page 184 of the appended authorship essay.
[†]*August 1572.* This date is inconsistent with H.W.'s provided above on page 2, suggesting that the August date should be 1571, or alternatively that H.W.'s January date should be 1573; the inconsistency provides a clue to H.W.'s identity with G.T. and hence with the author himself.
[†]*aliquid salis.* something of salt; substance.

occasion whereupon it was written—as they themselves did always with the verse rehearse unto me the cause that then moved them to write—I did with more labor gather them into some order and so placed them in this register, wherein as near as I could guess I have set in the first places those which Master F.J. did compile. And to begin with this his history that ensueth, it was—as he declared unto me—written upon this occasion: the said F.J. chanced once in the north parts of this realm to fall in company of a very fair gentlewoman whose name was Mistress Elinor, unto whom bearing a hot affection, he first adventured to write this letter following.

G.T.

Mistress I pray you understand that, being altogether a stranger in these parts, my good hap hath been to behold you to my—no small—contentation, and my evil hap accompanies the same with such imperfection of my deserts as that I find always a ready repulse in mine own forwardness. So that considering the natural climate of the country, I must say that I have found fire in frost. And yet comparing the inequality of my deserts with the least part of your worthiness, I feel a continual frost in my most fervent fire. Such is then the extremity of my passions, the which I could never have been content to commit unto this telltale paper, were it not that I am destitute of all other help. Accept therefore, I beseech you, the earnest good will of a more trusty than worthy servant, who being thereby encouraged, may supply the defects of his ability with ready trial of dutiful loyalty. And let this poor paper, besprent[†] with salt tears and blown over with scalding sighs, be saved

---

[†]*besprent.* sprinkled.

6

of you as a safeguard for your sampler, or a bottom[†] to wind your sewing silk, that when your last needle full is wrought, you may return to reading thereof and consider the care of him who is

More yours than his own.

F.J.

This letter by her received, as I have heard him say, her answer was this. She took occasion one day at his request to dance with him, the which doing, she bashfully began to declare unto him that she had read over the writing which he delivered unto her with like protestation that—as at delivery thereof, she understood not for what cause he thrust the same into her bosom—so now she could not perceive thereby any part of his meaning, nevertheless at last seemed to take upon her the matter, and though she disabled herself, yet gave him thanks as &c. Whereupon he brake the brawl[†] and walking abroad devised immediately these few verses following.

G.T.

Fair Bersabe[†] the bright once bathing in a well,
With dew bedimmed King David's eyes that rulèd Israél.
And Solomon himself, the source of sapiénce,
Against the force of such assaults could make but small defense:
To it the stoutest yield and strongest feel like woe,
Bold Hercules and Sampson both did prove it to be so.
What wonder seemeth then, when stars stand thick in skies,
If such a blazing star have power to dim my dazzled eyes?

[†]*bottom.* a spool, reel, or ball for winding thread; cf. footnote on page 13 and the discussion in the following essay for another meaning.
[†]*brawl.* a line dance.
[†]*Bersabe.* Bathsheba, wife of Urias and mistress to King David, as related in the book of *Samuel.*

SECRET SHAKESPEARE'S

Lenvoy[†]

To you these few suffice, your wits be quick and good,
You can conject by change of hue what humors feed my blood.

F.J.

I have heard the author say that these were the first verses that ever he[†] wrote upon like occasion, the which considering the matter precedent may in my judgment be well
allowed. And to judge his doing by the effects, he declared
unto me that before he could put the same in legible writing, it pleased the said Mistress Elinor of her courtesy[†] thus
to deal with him.

Walking in a garden among divers other gentlemen and
gentlewomen, with a little frowning smile in passing by
him, she delivered unto him a paper with these words:

"For that I understand not," quoth she, "th'intent of your
letters, I pray you take them here again and bestow them at
your pleasure," the which done and said, she passed by
without change either of pace or countenance.

F.J. somewhat troubled with her angry look did suddenly leave the company and walking into a park near adjoining, in great rage began to wreak his malice on this poor
paper and the same did rend and tear[†] in pieces, when suddenly at a glance he perceived it was not of his own handwriting, and therewithal abashed, upon better regard he per-

---

[†]*lenvoy*. a concise concluding stanza, often dedicatory and summary in
nature; from French *l'envoy*, with *envoi* the preferred modern spelling.
[†]*ever he*. a pun on our author *E. Vere*; cf. the essay following the novel,
Chapter 2 of *Shakespeare's Fingerprints*, and *Never and For Ever*.
[†]*her courtesy*. Pigman [2000] remarks that *courtesy* and its derivatives
appear fifty times in the novel, serving as a cover for *sex*, in which case
the courteous Moon, appearing at a later point in the novel, presents an
embarrassment for those not recognizing the author to be a nobleman.
[†]*tear*. reminiscent of the torn-letter motif in *Two Gentlemen of Verona*,
for which see the essay following.

ceived in one piece thereof written, in Roman, these letters
S H E. Wherefore placing all the pieces thereof as orderly
as he could, he found therein written these few lines hereafter following.

G.T.

Your sudden departure from our pastime yesterday
did enforce me for lack of chosen company to return
unto my work, wherein I did so long continue till at the
last the bare bottom did draw unto my remembrance
your strange request. And although I found therein no
just cause to credit your colored words, yet have I
thought good hereby to requite you with like courtesy,
so that at least you shall not condemn me for ungrate-
ful. But as to the matter therein contained, if I could
persuade myself that there were in me any coals to
kindle such sparks of fire, I might yet peradventure be
drawn to believe that your mind were frozen with like
fear. But as no smoke ariseth where no coal is kindled,
so without cause of affection the passion is easy to be
cured. This is all that I understand of your dark letters
and as much as I mean to answer.

S H E

My friend F.J. hath told me divers times that immediately upon receipt hereof, he grew in jealousy that the same
was not her own device. And therein I have no less allowed
his judgment than commended his invention of the verses
and letters before rehearsed. For as by the style this letter of
hers bewrayeth that it was not penned by a woman's capacity, so the sequel of her doings may decipher that she had
mo' ready clerks than trusty servants in store. Well, yet as
the perfect hound when he hath chased the hurt deer amid
the whole herd will never give over till he have singled it

again, even so F.J.,[†] though somewhat abashed with this doubtful show, yet still constant in his former intention, ceased not by all possible means to bring this deer yet once again to the bows, whereby she might be the more surely stricken and so in the end enforced to yield. Wherefore he thought not best to commit the said verses willingly into her custody, but privily lost them in her chamber, written in counterfeit, and after on the next day thought better to reply, either upon her or upon her secretary, in this wise as here followeth.

G.T.

The much that you have answered is very much, and much more than I am able to reply unto. Nevertheless in mine own defense, thus much I allege: that if my sudden departure pleased not you, I cannot myself therewith be pleased as one that seeketh not to please many, and more desirous to please you than any.[†] The cause of mine affection, I suppose you behold daily. For, self-love[†] avoided, every wight[†] may judge of themselves as much as reason persuadeth, the which if it be in your good nature suppressed with bashfulness, then mighty love grant you may once behold my wan cheeks washed in woe that therein my salt

---

[†]*even so F.J.* with intended wordplay *even so* = *E.Vere 17th Oxford,* as the reader will soon discover, thereby revealing F.J. to be the Earl of Oxford.

[†]*not to please many, ... to please you than any.* complement of sorts to H.W.'s expression *as one that thought better to please a number by common commodity than to feed the humor of any private person,* found on page 1 above, confirming that the discourses of F.J. and H.W. were written by a single author.

[†]*self-love.* another Shakespearean theme, as in *Sonnet 62*:
> *Sin of **self-love** possesseth all mine eye,*
> *And all my soul, and all my every part;*

[†]*wight.* person, individual.

tears may be a mirror to represent your own shadow and that like unto Narcissus you may be constrained to kiss the cold waves, wherein your counterfeit is so lively portrayed. For if abundance of other matters failed to draw my gazing eyes in contemplation of so rare excellency, yet might these your letters both frame in me an admiration of such divine esprit and a confusion to my dull understanding which so rashly presumed to wander in this endless labyrinth. Such I esteem you, and thereby am become such, and Even *HE.*[†]

F.J.

This letter finished and fair written over,[†] his chance was to meet her alone in a gallery of the same house, where—as I have heard him declare—his manhood in this kind of combat[†] was first tried, and therein I can compare him to a valiant prince, who distressed with power of enemies had committed the safeguard of his person to treaty of ambassade, and suddenly, surprised with a camisado[†] in his own trenches, was enforced to yield as prisoner.

[†]*Even HE.* plausibly *Even* = *E. Vere,* with shades of *even so I* and *even so my friend F.J.* as cited on the previous page and the following.

[†]*fair written over.* written over by fair = Vere, **over** being a common play on the **O**xford **Ver**e.

[†]*combat.* a reference to sex expressed in classical combative terms, the tradition of *militia amoris,* including *friendly foe*; for what lies behind the tradition, see Leslie Cahoon's 1988 study "The Bed as Battlefield: Erotic Conquest and Military Metaphor in Ovid's *Amores,* published in *Transactions of the American Philological Association 118:* 293-307.

[†]*camisado.* attack in the night by soldiers wearing white shirts over armor for purposes of easy identification by comrades in arms; a Spanish past participle meaning 'shirted', cognate with English *camisole.*

11

Even so my friend F.J.,[†] lately overcome by the beautiful beams of this dame Elinor and having now committed his most secret intent to these late rehearsed letters, was at unwares encountered with his friendly foe and constrained either to prepare some new defense or else like a recreant to yield himself as already vanquished. Wherefore, as in a trance, he lifted up his dazzled eyes and so continued in a certain kind of admiration not unlike the astronomer, who, having after a whole night's travail, in the gray morning found his desired star, hath fired his hungry eyes to behold the comet long looked for. Whereat this gracious dame, as one that could discern the sun before her chamber windows were wide open, did deign to embolden the fainting knight with these or like words:

"I perceive now," quod she, "how mishap doth follow me, that having chosen this walk for a simple solace, I am here disquieted by the man that meaneth my destruction," and therewithal, as half angry, began to turn her back when as my friend F.J. now awaked, 'gan thus salute her.

"Mistress," quod he, "and I perceive now the good hap haunts me, for being by lack of opportunity constrained to commit my welfare unto these blabbing leaves of bewraying paper"—showing them in his hand. "I am here recomforted with happy view of my desired joy," and therewithal reverently kissing his hand, did softly distrain[†] her slender arm and so stayed her departure.

The first blow thus proffered and defended, they walked and walked traversing divers[†] ways, wherein I doubt not but that my friend F.J. could quit himself reasonably well. And though it stood not with duty of a friend that I should

---

[†]*Even so my friend F.J.* yet another play on the author's name and title, *E. Vere, Seventeenth Oxford,* as also on page 10, here with an added bawdy innuendo and pun via the following item *overcome.*
[†]*distrain.* seize.
[†]*traversing divers.* unmistakable pun on *Vere* and *de Vere,* respectively.

therein require to know his secrets, yet of himself he declared thus much, that after long talk she was contented to accept his proffered service, but yet still disabling herself and seeming to marvel what cause had moved him to subject his liberty so willfully, or at least in a prison—as she termed it—so unworthy. Whereunto I need not rehearse his answer, but suppose now that thus they departed, saving I had forgotten this: she required of him the last rehearsed letter, saying that his first was lost and now she lacked a new bottom for her silk,[†] the which I warrant you, he granted, and so proffering to take a humble *congé*[†] by *bezo las manos*,[†] she graciously gave him the *zuccado dez labros*,[†] and so, for then, departed.

[†]*bottom for her silk.* a possible pun on the author's worm or vermin; hence, a play on **Vere**, with *silk* also supporting a bawdy interpretation, the connection effected via *bottom,* a word denoting the cocoon of the silkworm, further discussion to be found in Section 4 of the essay following the novel; for a less bawdy interpretation, cf. page 7.

[†]*congé.* departure with ceremonial bow.

[†]*bezo las manos.* I kiss your hands.

[†]*gave him the zuccado dez labros.* threw him a kiss; *zuccado* relates to the fencing term *stoccato* or *stoccata,* 'a thrust with palm in supination', i.e. upright as when throwing a kiss; the conceit includes a hint of sweetness via *zuccare,* 'sugar'; related usage is found in the author's *Menaphon* written under his *Greene* pseudonym, a name the author no doubt chose deliberately as translational cognate with the root *ver-*:

> *Pleusidippus, whose courteous inclination could not withstand this submission, in sign of reconcilement* **gave her a stoccado des labies.**

Pigman [2000: 565] misses the connection, confessing: "The only other instance of the phrase I can find occurs in Grange, who doubtless took it from here", i.e. from *Freeman.* Despite such confident doubtlessness, Pigman fails to recognize that *Grange* is another mask for our author and that he accordingly had no need to lift the expression from his earlier work; for discussion, see *Never and For Ever.*

A related missed example is found in Act I, Scene 3 of the tragedy of *Locrine,* where the clownish cobbler Strumbo bawdily remarks that Dorothy *"shall have the* **succado de labres***, and something else."*

And thereupon recounting her words, he compiled these following which he termed *terza sequenza,*[†] to sweet Mistress SHE.

Of thee dear dame, three lessons would I learn,
What reason first persuades the foolish fly
As soon as she a candle can discern
To play with flame, till she be burnt thereby?

Or what may move the mouse to bite the bait
Which strikes the trap that stops her hungry breath?
What calls the bird, where snares of deep deceit
Are closely couched to draw her to her death?

Consider well what is the cause of this,
And though percase thou wilt not so confess,
Yet deep desire to gain a heavenly bliss,[†]
May drown the mind in dole and dark distress

Oft is it seen, whereat my heart may bleed,
Fools play so long till they be caught indeed.

And then
It is a heaven to see them hop and skip,
And seek all shifts to shake their shackles off:

[†]*terza sequenza.* poem composed of three parts or stanzas.
[†]*Yet deep desire to gain a heavenly bliss.* This, together with preceding line, relates to a couplet found in the fourth act of *Love's Labor's Lost*, embracing not only the sequence *not so*, but also a similar image framed with the aid of *to gain a heavenly bliss* here and *to win a paradise* in the play. Analogous 'fingerprints' confirm that the man behind the *Shakespeare* pseudonym was the author of *Freeman Jones;* cf. the next note.

> *If by me broke, what fool is not so wise*
> *To lose an oath to win a paradise?*

It is a world, to see them hang the lip,
Who, erst, at love, were wont to scorn[†] and scoff.

But as the mouse, once caught in crafty trap,
May bounce and beat, against the boarden wall,
Till she have brought her head in such mishap,
That down to death her fainting limbs must fall.

And as the fly once singèd in the flame,
Cannot command her wings to wave away,
But by the heel, she hangeth in the same
Till cruèl death her hasty journey stay.

So they that seek to break the links of love
Strive with the stream and this by pain I prove.[†]

For when
I first beheld that heavenly hue of thine,
Thy stately stature and thy comely grace,
I must confess these dazzled eyes of mine
Did wink for fear, when I first viewed thy face:

But bold desire did open them again,
And had me look till I had looked too long,
I pitied them that did procure my pain,
And loved the looks that wrought me all the wrong:

[†]***love*** *... **to scorn**.* reminiscent of *Venus and Adonis* with respect to both lexicon and meaning: *Hunting he loved, but **love** he laughed **to scorn**;* for related examples, see *Never and For Ever*.

[†]***love*** *... **and this by pain I prove**.* reminiscent of the terminal couplet of Shakespeare's *Sonnet 154,* with identical rhyming words:

> *Came there for cure, **and this by** that **I prove**,*
> *Love's fire heats water, water cools not **love**.*

And as the bird once caught, but works her woe,
That strives to leave the limèd twigs[†]behind:
Even so the more I strave to part thee fro,
The greater grief did grow within my mind:

Remediless then must I yield to thee,
And crave no more, thy servant but to be.
Till then and ever.[†] HE. F.J.

When he had well sorted this sequence, he sought opportunity to leave it where she might find it before it were lost. And now the coals began to kindle, whereof but erewhile[†] she feigned herself altogether ignorant. The flames began to break out on every side and she, to quench them, shut up herself in her chamber solitarily. But as the smithy gathers greater heat by casting on of water, even so the more she absented herself from company, the fresher was the grief which galded[†] her remembrance, so that at last the report was spread through the house that Mistress Elinor was sick, at which news F.J. took small comfort.

Nevertheless Dame Venus with good aspect did yet thus much further his enterprise. The dame—whether it were by sudden change or of wonted custom—fell one day into a

---

[†]*limèd twigs.* twigs covered with adhesive birdlime used to catch birds, as also featured under the author's *Shakespeare* pseudonym.
[†]*ever.* a play on the author's family name, again suggesting that F.J. is modeled on de Vere, with initial *F.* of *F.J.* a play on the name *Vere* via **Free**man; transformation of *Freeman* to *Fernando* in the revised version of *Freeman* renders the intended wordplay ever more transparent.
[†]*erewhile.* after a while.
[†]*galded.* galled, with intrusive *d,* as in the initial quatrain of Shakespeare's *Sonnet 71:*

> *No longer mourn for me when I am dead*
> *Than you shall hear the surly sullen bell*
> *Give warning to the world that I am fled*
> *From this vile world with **vildest** worms to dwell.*

16

great bleeding at the nose,[†] for which accident the said F.J. amongst other pretty conceits hath apparent remedy, whereby he took occasion—when they of the house had all in vain sought many ways to stop her bleeding—to work his feat in this wise. First he pleaded ignorance as though he knew not her name and therefore demanded the same of one other gentlewoman in the house whose name was Mistress Frances, who when she had to him declared that her name was Elinor, he said these words or very like in effect:

"If I thought I should not offend Mistress Elinor, I would not doubt to stop her bleeding without either pain or difficulty."

This gentlewoman, somewhat tickled with his words, did incontinent make relation thereof to the said Mistress Elinor, who immediately—declaring that F.J. was her late receivèd servant—returned the said messenger unto him with especial charge that he should employ his devoire[†] towards the recovery[†] of her health, with whom the same F.J. repaired to the chamber of his desired, and finding her set in a chair, leaning on the one side over a silver basin. After his due reverence, he laid his hand on her temples and privily rounding her in her ear, desired her to command a hazel[†] stick and a knife, the which being brought, he delivered unto her, saying on this wise.

"Mistress I will speak certain words in secret to myself and do require no more but when you hear me say openly

---

[†]*bleeding at the nose.* associated with sexual desire.

[†]*devoire.* duty, what is due her, with plausible identification of the servant as the author *de Vere.*

[†]*recovery.* play on *Oxford Vere* via *recovery,* with possible erotic innuendo in terms of the verb *cover.*

[†]*hazel.* choice of hazel wood probably relates to rhabdomancy, a widespread earlier tradition comprehending the utilization of hazel sticks or wands for divination, augury, and related ends; conjecturally related to the classical caduceus, symbolic of healing.

this word *amen,* that you with this knife will make a nick upon this hazel stick. And when you have made five nicks, command me also to cease."

The dame, partly of good will to the knight and partly to be staunched of her bleeding, commanded her maid and required the other gentles somewhat to stand aside, which done, he began his orations, wherein he had not long muttered before he pronounced *amen,* wherewith the lady made a nick on the stick with her knife. The said F.J. continued to another *amen,* when the lady, having made another nick, felt her bleeding began to staunch, and so by the third *amen* thoroughly staunched.

F.J. then changing his prayers into private talk said softly unto her: "Mistress, I am glad that I am hereby enabled to do you some service, and as the staunching of your own blood may some way recomfort you, so if the shedding of my blood may any way content you, I beseech you command it, for it shall be evermore[†] readily employed in your service," and therewithal with a loud voice pronounced *amen.*

Wherewith the good lady making a nick did secretly answer thus: "Good servant," quod she, "I must needs think myself right happy to have gained your service and good will, and be you sure that although there be in me no such desert as may draw you into this depth of affection, yet such as I am, I shall be always glad to show myself thankful unto you, and now, if you think yourself assured that I shall bleed no more, do then pronounce your fifth *amen,*" the which pronounced, she made also her fifth nick and held up her head, calling the company unto her and declaring unto them that her bleeding was thoroughly staunched.

[†]*evermore.* a plausible play on *E. Vere,* as also *overlong* below and several undaggered items on the previous page.

Well, it were long to tell what sundry opinions were pro-nounced upon this act, and I do dwell overlong in the discourses of this F.J., especially having taken in hand only to copy out his verses, but for the circumstance both better declare the effect, I will return to my former tale.

F.J. tarrying a while in the chamber found opportunity to lose his sequence near to his desirèd mistress, and after *congé* taken, departed, after whose departure the lady arose out of her chair and her maid going about to remove the same espied and took up the writing, the which her mistress perceiving, 'gan suddenly conjecture that the same had in it some like matter to the verses once before left in like man-ner and made semblance to mistrust that the same should be some words of conjuration, and taking it from her maid did peruse it and immediately said to the company that she would not forgo the same for a great treasure.

But to be plain, I think that—F.J. excepted—she was glad to be rid of all company until she had with sufficient leisure turned over and retossed every[†] card in this sequ-ence,[†] and not long after being now tickled through all the veins with an unknown humor, adventured of herself to commit unto a like ambassador the deciphering of that which hitherto she had kept more secret and thereupon wrote with her own hand and head in this wise.

G.T.

Good servant, I am out of all doubt much beholding unto you and I have great comfort by your means in the staunching of my blood. And I take great comfort to read your letters and I have found in my chamber divers[†] songs which I think to be of your making, and I

[†]*every.* another possible play on *E. Vere.*
[†]*sequence.* the poetry sequence.
[†]*divers.* de Vere's.

promise you they are excellently made, and I assure you
that I will be ready to do for you any pleasure that I can
during my life. Wherefore I pray you come to my
chamber once in a day till I come abroad again, and I
will be glad of your company and for because that you
have promised to be my HE, I will take upon me this
name,

your SHE.

    This letter I have seen of her own handwriting and as
therein the reader may find great difference of style from
her former letter, so may you now understand the cause.
She had in the same house a friend, a servant, a secretary.
What should I name him? Such one as she esteemed in time
past more than was cause in time present, and to make my
tale good, I will—by report of my very[†] good friend F.J.—
describe him unto you. He was in height the proportion of
two pygmies, in breadth the thickness of two bacon hogs,
of presumption a giant, of power a gnat, apishly witted,
knavishly mannered, and crabbedly savored. What was
there in him then to draw a fair lady's liking? Marry sir,
even all in all, a well-lined purse, wherewith he could at
every call provide such pretty conceits as pleased her peevish fantasy, and by that means he had thoroughly, long
before, insinuated himself with this amorous dame.
    This manling,[†] this minion, this slave, this secretary,
was now by occasion ridden to London forsooth, and
though his absence were unto her a disfurnishing of eloquence, it was yet unto F.J. an opportunity of good advantage, for when he perceived the change of her style and
thereby grew in some suspicion that the same proceeded by
absence of her chief chancellor, he thought good now to

[†]*very good friend F.J.* In other words F.J. is Vere.
[†]*manling.* little man.

smite while the iron was hot and to lend his mistress such a pen[†] in her secretary's absence as he should never[†] be able at his return to amend the well[†] writing thereof, wherefore according to her command he repaired once every day to her chamber at the least, whereas he guided himself so well and could devise such store of sundry pleasure and pastimes that he grew in favor not only with his desired, but also with the rest of the gentlewomen.

And one day passing the time amongst them, their play grew to this end that his mistress being Queen demanded of him these three questions.

"Servant," quod she, "I charge you as well upon your allegiance being now my subject, as also upon your fidelity, having vowed your service unto me, that you answer me these three questions by the very truth[†] of your secret thought. First, what thing in this universal world doth most rejoice and comfort you?"

F.J. abasing his eyes towards the ground took good advisement in his answer, when a fair gentlewoman of the company clapped him on the shoulder saying:

"How now sir, is your hand on your halfpenny?"[†]

To whom he answered: "No fair lady, my hand is on my heart and yet my heart is not in mine own hands," where-

---

[†]*pen.* bawdy, as indicated in the note on page 92, as also in the essay.

[†]*he ... never.* signifying 'he … Ned Vere', *Ned* being a nickname for *Edward.*

[†]*amend the well.* playing on *well* as the female pudendum.

[†]*very truth.* a double play on the author's family name, *very* being clear, *truth* being an instance of *ver*-play via translation, as in the Vere family's punning motto *Vero Nihil Verius,* 'nothing truer than truth', or equivalently, 'nothing truer than a Vere'; in the next sentence *universal* may also be taken as a play on the author's name and on his real-life mistress (in view of the discussion of *Una* in the essay following) with juxtaposition as *uni-ver.*

[†]*hand on your halfpenny.* referring proverbially to a selfish goal and bawdily to F.J.'s semi-erection, i.e. his half peni(s).

withal abashed, turning towards Dame Elinor, he said: "My sovereign[†] and mistress, according to the charge of your command and the duty that I owe you, my tongue shall bewray unto you the truth of mine intent. At this present a reward given me without desert doth so rejoice me with continual remembrance thereof that though my mind be so occupied to think thereon, as that day nor night I can be quiet[†] from that thought; yet the joy and pleasure which I conceive in the same[†] is such that I can neither be cloyed with continuance thereof, nor yet afraid that any mishap can countervail[†] so great a treasure. This is to me such a heaven to dwell in[†] as that I feed by day and repose by night upon the fresh record of this reward."

This, as he sayeth, he meant by the kiss that she lent him in the gallery and by the profession of her last letters and words. Well, though this answer be somewhat misty, yet let my friend's excuse be that taken upon the sudden[†] he thought better to answer darkly than to be mistrusted openly.

Her second question was what thing in this life did most grieve his heart and disquiet his mind. Whereunto he answered that although his late rehearsèd joy were incomparable, yet the greatest enemy that disturbed the same was the

---

[†]*my sovereign.* for possible significance, see the essay following as it touches on the identification of Elinor.

[†]*my mind ... day ... night ... quiet.* congruent with the terminal couplet of *Sonnet 43,* published under the author's *Shake-speare* pseudonym.

*Lo thus by **day** my limbs, by **night my mind**,*
*For thee, and for myself, no **quiet** find.*

[†]*in the same.* in Elinor's treasure, giving grounds for subsequent sexual innuendo.

[†]*countervail.* another covert play on Elinor's treasure.

[†]*to dwell in.* i.e. in Elinor's treasure.

[†]*upon the sudden.* at the moment.

privy worm[†] of his own guilty conscience which accused him evermore[†] with great unworthiness and that this was his greatest grief.

The lady, biting upon the bit at his cunning[†] answers made unto these two questions, 'gan thus reply: "Servant, I had thought to have touched you yet nearer with my third question, but I will refrain to attempt your patience, and now for my third demand, answer me directly in what manner this passion doth handle you and how these contraries may hang together by any possibility of concord, for your words are strange."

F.J. now rousing himself boldly took occasion thus to handle his answer: "Mistress," quod he, "my words indeed are strange, but yet my passion is much stranger, and thereupon this other day, to content mine own fantasy, I devised a sonnet, which although it be a piece of cocklorel's[†] music, and such as I might be ashamed to publish in this company, yet because my truth[†] in this answer may the better appear unto you, I pray you vouchsafe to receive the same in writing," and drawing a paper out of his pocket, presented it unto her, wherein was written this sonnet.

G.T.

Love, hope, and death, do stir in me such strife,
As never man[†] but I led such a life.

[†]*worm.* a potential double play, (*i*) on the name *Vere* via translation into Latin, cf. the English borrowing *vermiform,* and (*ii*) on Vere's member.
[†]*him evermore.* i.e. him E. Vere.
[†]*cunning.* wanton wordplay motivated by F.J.'s references to dwelling in Elinor's treasure, giving still more reason for her biting on the bit.
[†]*cocklorel's.* allusion to an early sixteenth century work entitled *Cocke Lorelles Bote,* considered trifling.
[†]*my truth.* my identity as Vere, *truth* being a *ver*-word related to *verity,* as noted above on page 21.
[†]*never man.* **Ned Vere,** *Ned* being a common nickname for *Edward.*

First burning love doth wound my heart to death,
And when death comes at call of inward grief,
Cold lingering hope doth feed my fainting breath
Against my will, and yields my wound relief:
So that I live, but yet my life is such,
As death would never grieve me half so much.

No comfort then but only this I taste,
To salve such sore, such hope will never want,
And with such hope, such life will ever last,[†]
And with such life, such sorrows are not scant.
O strange desire, O[†] *life with torments tossed*
Through too much hope, mine only hope is lost.
                    Even HE.   F.J.

This sonnet was highly commended and in my judgment it deserveth no less. I have heard F.J. say that he borrowed th'invention of an Italian,[†] but were it a translation or invention, if I be judge, it is both pretty and pithy.

His duty thus performed, their pastimes ended, and at their departure, for a watchword he counseled his mistress by little and little to walk abroad, saying that the gallery

---

[†]*never want ... ever last.* two puns on the family name *Vere.*
[†]*O.* common play on the author's **O**xford title, documented in Chapters 0 and 4 of *Shakespeare's Fingerprints*; the whole *sesta rima* stanza, quatrain plus couplet, is reminiscent of a stanza associated with the author's real name, which includes the *ver*-pun *I hover* alongside *tower* and *hower,* the latter for present-day *hour.*

Lo thus I live twixt fear and comfort tossed,
With least abode where best I feel content;
I seld' resort where I should settle most,
My sliding times too soon with her are spent.
*I hover high and soar where Hope doth **tower**,*
*Yet froward Fate defers my happy **hower**.*

[†]*Italian.* Prouty [1942: 246] pegged the Italian as Petrarch, and the poem itself as relating to CXXIV of his *Rime.*

near adjoining was so pleasant as if he were half dead, he thought that by walking therein he might be half and more revived.

"Think you so, servant?" quod she. "And the last time that I walked there I suppose I took the cause of my malady, but by your advice, and for you have so clerkly staunched my bleeding, I will assay to walk there tomorrow."

"Mistress," quod he, "and in more full accomplishment of my duty towards you and in sure hope that you will use the same only to your own private commodity, I will there await upon you and between you and me will teach you the full order how to staunch the bleeding of any creature, whereby you shall be as cunning as myself."

"Gramercy† good servant," quod she. "I think you lost the same in writing here yesterday, but I cannot understand it and therefore tomorrow, if I feel myself anything amended, I will send for you thither to entrust† me thoroughly."

Thus they departed, and at suppertime, the knight of the castle finding fault that his guest's stomach served him no better began to accuse the grossness of his viands† to whom one of the gentlewomen which had passed the afternoon in his company answered:

"Nay sir," quod she. "This gentleman hath a passion the which once in a day at the least doth kill his appetite."

"Are you so well acquainted with the disposition of his body?" quod the Lord of the house.

"By his own saying," quod she, "and not otherwise."

"Fair lady," quod F.J., "you either mistook me or overheard me then, for I told of a comfortable humor which so fed me with continual remembrance of joy as that my sto-

---

†*gramercy.* thanks, via French *grand merci.*
†*entrust.* with a hint of *enthrust.*
†*viands.* food; derivative of Romance root *viv-*, as in modern English *vivid*, *vivacious*, and *revive.*

25

mach being full thereof doth desire in manner none other vittles."

"Why sir," quod the host, "do you then live by love?"

"God forbid, Sir," quod F.J., "for then my cheeks would be much thinner than they be, but there are divers[†] other greater causes of joy than the doubtful lots of love, and for mine own part, to be plain, I cannot love and I dare not hate."

"I would I thought so," quod the gentlewoman.

And thus with pretty nips, they passed over their supper, which ended, the Lord of the house required F.J. to dance and pass the time with the gentlewoman, which he refused not to do. But suddenly, before the music was well tuned, came out Dame Elynor[†] in her night attire and said to the lord that—supposing the solitariness of her chamber had increased her malady—she came out for her better recreation to see them dance.

"Well done daughter," quod the Lord.

"And I, Mistress," quod F.J., "would gladly bestow the leading of you about this great chamber to drive away the faintness of your fever."

"No, good servant," quod the Lady, "but in my stead, I pray you dance with this fair gentlewoman," pointing him to the lady that had so taken him up at supper.

F.J. to avoid mistrust did agree to her request without further entreaty. The dance begun, this knight marched on with the image of Saint Frances in his hand and Saint Elynor in his heart. The violands[†] at end of the pavion[†] stayed a while, in which time this dame said to F.J. in this wise:

[†]*divers.* authorial code for *de Vere's.*

[†]*Elynor.* alternate spelling to underscore Elinor's inconstant nature.

[†]*violands.* a sixteenth century stringed instrument.

[†]*pavion.* stately court dance; modern *pavan,* derivative of the *Paduana* by origination in *Padua.*

"I am right sorry for you in two respects, although the familiarity have hitherto had no great continuance between us and as I do lament your case,[†] so do I rejoice—for mine own contentation—that I shall now see a due trial of the experiment which I have long desired."

This said, she kept silence, when F.J., somewhat astonied with her strange speech, thus answered: "Mistress, although I cannot conceive the meaning of your words, yet by courtesy I am constrained to yield you thanks for your good will, the which appeareth no less in lamenting of mishaps than in rejoicing at good fortune. What experiment you mean to try by me, I know not, but I dare assure you that my skill in experiments is very simple."

Herewith the instruments sounded a new measure and they passed forthwards, leaving to talk until the noise ceased, which done, the gentlewoman replied: "I am sorry sir that you did erewhile[†] deny love and all his laws and that in so open audience."

"Not so," quod F.J., "but as the word was roundly taken, so can I readily answer it by good reason."

"Well," quod she, "how if the hearers will admit no reasonable answer?"

"My reason shall yet be, nevertheless," quod he, "in reasonable judgment."

Herewith she smiled and he cast a glance towards Dame Elinor askances[†]: "Art thou pleased?"

[†]*your case.* with play on Elinor's pudendum in light of the preceding **continuance,** the following **contentation,** and analogous bawdy play elsewhere, as in Act I, Scene 3 of *All's Well That Ends Well,* where Lavatch entreats the countess: *I do beg your good will in this **case,*** who replies: *In what **case?*** Lavatch continues: *In Isbel's **case*** with a clear bawdy reference in view of his clarification: *I shall never have the blessing of God till I have issue o' my body ...*
[†]*erewhile.* a while ago.
[†]*askances.* as if to say, but compare Pigman [2000: 570].

Again the viols called them forthwards and again at the end of the brawl said F.J. to this gentlewoman: "I pray you, Mistress, and what may be the second cause of your sorrow sustained in my behalf?

"Nay soft," quod she, "percase I have not yet told you the first, but content yourself, for the second cause you shall never know at my hands, until I see due trial of the experiment which I have long desired."

"Why then," quod he, "I can but wish a present occasion to bring the same to effect, to the end that I might also understand the mystery of your meaning."

"And so might you fail of your purpose," quod she, "for I mean to be better assured of him that shall know the depth of mine intent in such a secret than I do suppose that any creature—one except—may be of you."

"Gentlewoman," quod he, "you speak Greek, the which I have now forgotten and mine instructors are too far from me at this present to expound your words."

"Or else too near,"[†] quod she, and so smiling stayed her talk, when the music called them to another dance, which ended, F.J. half afraid of false suspect and more amazed at this strange talk, gave over, and bringing Mistress Frances to her place was thus saluted by his mistress:

"Servant," quod she, "I had done you great wrong to have danced with you, considering that this gentlewoman and you had former occasion of so weighty conference."

"Mistress," said F.J., "you had done me great pleasure, for by our conference I have but brought my brains in a busy conjecture."

"I doubt not," said his mistress, "but you will end that business easily."

"It is hard," said F.J., "to end the thing whereof yet I have found no beginning."

[†]*too near.* that is, she too near him as instructor in the experiment.

His mistress with change of countenance kept silence, whereat Dame Frances rejoicing, cast out this bone to gnaw on: "I perceive," quod she, "it is evil to halt before a cripple."

F.J., perceiving now that his mistress waxed angry, thought good on her behalf thus to answer: "And it is evil to hop before them that run for the bell."[†]

His mistress replied: "And it is evil to hang the bell at their heels which are always running."[†]

The Lord of the castle, overhearing these proper quips, rose out of his chair and coming towards F.J., required him to dance a galliard.[†]

"Sir," said F.J., "I have hitherto at your appointment but walked about the house. Now if you be desirous to see one tumble a turn or twain, it is like enough that I might provoke you to laugh at me, but in good faith my dancing days are almost done. And therefore sir," quod he, "I pray you speak to them that are more nimble at tripping on the toe."

Whilst he was thus saying, Dame Elynor had made her congey[†] and was now entering the door of her chamber, when F.J., all amazed at her sudden departure, followed to take leave of his mistress, but she more than angry refused to hear his goodnight and entering the chamber caused her maid to clap the door.

F.J. with heavy cheer returned to his company, and Mistress Frances, to touch his sore with a corrosive, said to him softly in this wise: "Sir you may now perceive that this our

---

[†]*run for the bell.* pursue the prize, raising the question whether the prize was Elinor or F.J. himself.

[†]*evil to hang ... always running.* i.e. evil for Elinor, who runs after men to so win the prize.

[†]*galliard.* spirited triple time dance imported from France.

[†]*congey.* variant of *congé* with stress on initial syllable; modern *congee.*

country cannot allow the French manner of dancing, for they as I have heard tell do more commonly dance to talk than entreat to dance."

F.J. hoping to drive out one nail with another, and thinking this a mean most convenient to suppress all jealous supposes, took Mistress Frances by the hand and with a heavy smile answered: "Mistress, and I, because I have seen the French manner of dancing, will eftsoons entreat you to dance a bargenet."[†]

"What mean you by this?" quod Mistress Frances.

"If it please you to follow," quod he, "you shall see that I can jest without joy and laugh without lust," and calling the musicians, caused them softly to sound the tintarnell,[†] when he clearing his voice did *alla Napolitana* apply these verses following, unto the measure.

G.T.

In prime of lusty years[†] *when Cupid caught me in,*
And nature taught the way to love, how I might best begin:
To please my wand'ring eye, in beauty's tickle trade,
To gaze on each that passèd by, a careless sport I made.

With sweet enticing bait, I fished for many a dame
And warmèd me by many a fire, yet felt I not the flame:
But when at last I spied that face that pleased me most,
The coals were quick, the wood was dry, and I began to toast.

[†]*bargenet.* pastoral or rustic dance.
[†]*tintarnell.* music of uncertain nature, but with plausible reference to *Elinor* via *Nell,* and thus to her real-life inspiration.
[†]*in prime of lusty years.* a phrase in no sense commonplace, utilized by the author under one of his many veronyms, namely *Geffrey Whitney: A youthful prince in prime of lusty years*. More empirical confirmation of its pseudonymous status will be found in *Never and for Ever.*

30

ADVENTURES OF FREEMAN JONES

And smiling yet full oft, I have beheld that face,
When in my heart[†] I might bewail mine own unlucky case:
And oft again with looks that might bewray my grief,
I pleaded hard for just reward[†] and sought to find relief.

What will you more? So oft, my gazing eyes did seek
To see the rose and lily strive[†] upon that lively cheek:
Till at the last I spied and by good proof I found,
That in that face was painted plain, the piercer of my wound.

Then, all too late,[†] aghast, I did my foot retire,
And sought with secret sighs to quench my greedy scalding fire:

[†]***full oft ... face ... my heart.*** congruent with the following lines drawn
from *Romeus and Juliet* of 1562, also penned by our novelist as demon-
strated in Chapter 10 of *Shakespeare's Fingerprints.*

> *His **face**'s rosy hue, I saw **full oft** to seek,*
> *And straight again it flashèd forth and spread in either cheek.*
> *His fixèd heavenly eyne that through me quite did pierce,*
> *His thoughts unto **my heart**, my thoughts they seeméd to rehearse.*

[†]***just reward.*** employed by the author under other pseudonyms, include-
ing R.W. in his *Forrest of Fancy.*

> *Good reader, reap his **just reward**, to recompense his mere good will,*
> *Receive his gift in grateful wise, and of the same conceive none ill.*

[†]*rose and lily strive.* The conceit of colors red (as of a rose or blush)
and white (as of a lily or virtue) striving on a cheek or face is typical of
Shakespeare:

> *When at Collatium this false lord arrived,*
> *Well was he welcomed by the Roman dame,*
> *Within whose **face** beauty and virtue **strived***
> *Which of them both should underprop her fame:*
> *When virtue bragged, beauty would blush for shame;*
> *When beauty boasted **blushes**, in despite*
> *Virtue would stain that o'er with silver **white**.*
> *Rape of Lucrece.*

[†]*all too late.* cf. following note.

But lo, I did prevail as much to guide my will,†
As he that seeks with halting heel to hop against the hill.

Or as the feeble sight, would search the sunny beam,
Even so I† found but labor lost, to strive against the stream.
Then 'gan I thus resolve, since liking forcèd love,
Should I mislike† my happy choice, before I did it prove?

And since none other joy I had but her to see,
Should I retire my deep desire†? No no it would not be:
Though great the duty were that she did well deserve,
And I poor man, unworthy am, so worthy a wight to serve.

Yet hope my comfort stayed that she would have regard
To my good will, that nothing craved,† but like for just reward:
I see the faucon gent† sometimes will take delight,
To seek the solace of her wing and dally with a kite.

---

†*guide **my will**.* plausible phallic reference in light of Shakespeare's *Sonnet 135.*

> *Wilt thou whose **will** is large and spacious,*
> *Not once vouchsafe to hide **my will** in thine,*
> *Shall **will** in others seem right gracious,*
> *And in **my will** no fair acceptance shine:*

Note further the local presence of *all too late* with *my will* to yield the result ***all too late** ... I ... **my will*** provides a clue to another of the author's pseudonyms, namely *John Grange,* who has a congruent line: *Then wish **I all too late** that Mars had ruled **my will**.* The collocation is found elsewhere in the volume comprising *Freeman.*

†*Even so I.* another pun identifying the author, used repeatedly.

†*mislike.* dislike.

†***deep desire**.* employed on page 14 and elsewhere in *Flowers,* but also in the author's Shakespeare opus, as a line from *Venus and Adonis: The sea hath bounds, but **deep desire** hath none.*

†*my good will ... nothing craved.* bawdy; *nothing* and *will* denote the female and male organs, respectively; for bawdy *will,* see the essay following the text; for bawdy *nothing,* see Chapter 0 of *Shakespeare's Fingerprints.*

†*faucon gent.* falcon gentle, one of several falcon types considered desirable to hawkers for being easily managed.

The fairest wolf will choose the foulest for her make,[†]
And why? Because he doth endure most sorrow for her sake:
Even so had I like hope, when doleful days were spent
When weary words were wasted well to open true intent.[†]

When floods of flowing tears had washed my weeping eyes,
When trembling tongue[†] had troubled her with loud lamenting cries:
At last her worthy will[†] would pity this my plaint,
And comfort me her own poor slave, whom fear had made so faint.

Wherefore I made a vow, the stony rock should start,
Ere I presume to let her slip out of my faithful heart.

Lenvoy.

And when she saw by proof the pith of my good will,
She took in worth this simple song for want of better skill:
And as my just deserts, her gentle heart did move,
She was content to answer thus: I am content to love.

These verses are more in number than do stand with
contentation of some judgments, and yet the occasion thoroughly considered, I can commend them with the rest, for it
is (as may be well termed) *continua oratio*,[†] declaring a full

---

[†]*the fairest wolf ... choose the foulest ... for her make.* i.e. for her mate;
Pigman [2000: 572] cites Pettie: "**the she wolf** who always **choseth**
that wolf **for her make** who is made most lean and **foul** by following
her," but fails to discern that *George Pettie* is another of our novelist's
pseudonyms, confirmed in Chapter 15 of *Shakespeare's Fingerprints*
and by the example of estrangement in the essay following the text.
[†]*wasted well to open true intent.* possibly bawdy.
[†]*trembling tongue.* associated with several of the author's pseudonyms,
including the veronym *Averell*: *Recovering of her former force, with*
***trembling tongue** she spake.*
[†]*her worthy will.* bawdy.
[†]*continua oratio.* continuous discourse, with a possible bawdy reading.

discourse[†] of his first love, wherein (over and besides[†] that the epithets are aptly applied and the verse of itself pleasant enough) I note that by it he meant in clouds to decipher unto Mistress Frances such matter as she would snatch at and yet could take no good hold of[†] the same. Furthermore, it answered very aptly to the note[†] which the music sounded, as the skillful reader by due trial may approve.

This singing dance or dancing song ended, Mistress Frances, giving due thanks, seemed weary also of the company, and proffering to depart, gave yet this farewell to F.J., not vexed with choler, but pleased with contentation[†] and called away by heavy sleep: "I am constrained,[†]" quod she, "to bid you good night," and so turning to the rest of the company, took her leave.

Then the Master of the house commanded a torch to light F.J. to his lodging, where—as I have heard him say— the sudden change of his mistress' countenance[†] together with the strangeness of Mistress Frances' talk made such an encounter in his mind that he could take no rest that night.[†] Wherefore in the morning rising very early—although it were far before his mistress' hour—he cooled his choler by

---

[†]*declaring a full discourse.* i.e. the full intercourse of his first love.

[†]*over and besides.* elaborating the nature of the intercourse, with *continua oratio* possibly intended bawdily as '*cont-in(ua) or(atio)*'.

[†]*such matter ... snatch at ... take no good hold of.* the matter deciphered is de Vere's pudendum, often given as his *will,* as in the preceding verse; *decipher* is itself a play on the name *de Vere.*

[†]*answered very ... to the note.* a play on *Ed Vere* via *answer-ed very,* who answers to the note, *note* being a play on the female pudendum.

[†]*pleased with contentation.* pleased by stimulation of that alluded to by the word *contentation.*

[†]*constrained.* strained by the stimulation referred to in the previous note.

[†]*his mistress' countenance.* again bawdy.

[†]*encounter ... no rest that night.* play on the subsequence *count* of *encounter,* explaining why F.J. could not sleep.

walking in the gallery near to her lodging and there in this passion compiled these verses following.

G.T.

A cloud of care hath covered all my coast,
And storms of strife do threaten to appear:
The waves of woe which I mistrusted most,
Have broke the banks wherein my life lay clear:
    Chips of ill chance are fallen amid my choice,
    To mar the mind that meant for to rejoice.

Before I sought, I found the haven of hap,
Wherein once found, I sought to shroud my ship,
But louring love hath lift me from her lap,
And crabbèd lot begins to hang the lip:
    The drops of dark mistrust do fall so thick,
    They pierce my coat and touch my skin at quick.[†]

What may be said where truth cannot prevail?
What plea may serve where will itself is judge?
What reason rules where right and reason fail?
Remediless then must the guiltless trudge:
    And seek out care to be the carving knife,
    To cut the thread that ling'reth such a life.

F.J.

This is but a rough meter and reason, for it was devised in great disquiet of mind and written in rage, yet have I seen much worse pass the musters, yea and where both the Lieutenant and Provost Marshal were men of ripe judgment. And as it is, I pray you let it pass here, for the truth is that F.J. himself had so slender liking thereof, or at least of

---

[†]*Before ... quick.* Pigman [2000] notes that this and the first stanza are inspired in part by Petrarch's *Canzoniere 189.*

one word escaped therein, that he never[†] presented it but to the matter.

When he had long—and all in vain—looked for the coming of his mistress into her appointed walk, he wandered into the park near adjoining to the castle wall, where his chance was to meet Mistress Frances accompanied with one other gentlewoman, by whom he passed with a reverence of courtesy, and so walking on came into the side of a thicket where he sat down under a tree to allay his sadness with solitariness.

Mistress Frances, partly of courtesy and affection and partly to content her mind by continuance of such talk as they had commenced overnight, entreated her companion to go with her unto this tree of reformation, whereas they found the knight with his arms unfolded in a heavy kind of contemplation, unto whom Mistress Frances stepped apace, right softly and at unwares[†] gave this salutation:

"I little thought Sir Knight," quod she, "by your evensong[†] yesternight to have found you presently at such a morrow massed,[†] but I perceive you serve your saint with double devotion and I pray God grant you treble meed[†] for your true intent."

F.J. taken thus upon the sudden could none otherwise answer but thus: "I told you Mistress," quod he, "that I could laugh without lust and jest without joy," and therewithal starting up with a more bold countenance, came towards the dames, proffering unto them his service to wait upon them homewards.

[†]*he never*. i.e. he Ned Vere.
[†]*at unwares*. unexpectedly.
[†]*evensong*. evening song with possible pun via *e ver song*.
[†]*massed*. related to *mass*, accounting for the mention of F.J.'s saint.
[†]*treble meed*. triple reward.

"I have heard say oft times," quod Mistress Frances, "that it is hard to serve two masters at one time, but we will be right glad of your company."

"I thank you," quod F.J., and so walking on with them, fell into sundry discourses, still refusing to touch any part of their former communication, until Mistress Frances said unto him: "By my troth," quod she, "I would be your debtor these two days, to answer me truly but unto one question that I will propound."

"Fair gentlewoman," quod he, "you shall not need to become my debtor, but if it please you to quit question by question, I will be more ready to gratify you in this request than either reason requireth or than you would be willing to work my contentation."

"Master F.J.," quod she, and that sadly, "peradventure you know but a little how willing I would be to procure your contentation, but you know that hitherto familiarity hath taken no deep root betwixt us twain. And though I find in you no manner of cause whereby I might doubt to commit this or greater matter unto you, yet have I stayed hitherto so to do in doubt lest you might thereby justly condemn me both of arrogancy and lack of discretion, wherewith I must yet foolishly affirm that I have with great pain bridled my tongue from disclosing the same unto you. Such is then the good will that I bear towards you, the which if you rather judge to be impudency than a friendly meaning, I may then curse the hour that I first concluded thus to deal with you."

Herewithal being now red for chaste bashfulness, she abased her eyes and stayed her talk, to whom F.J. thus answered: "Mistress Frances, if I should with so exceeding villainy requite such and so exceeding courtesy, I might not only seem to degenerate from all gentry, but also to differ in behavior from all the rest of my life spent. Wherefore to be plain with you in few words, I think myself so much bound unto you for divers respects, as if ability do not fail me, you shall find me mindful in requital of the same. And for disclosing your mind to me, you may if so please you adventure it without adventure, for by this sun," quod he, "I will not deceive such trust as you shall lay upon me, and furthermore, so far forth as I may, I will be yours in any respect. Wherefore I beseech you accept me for your faithful friend and so shall you surely find me."

"Not so," quod she, "but you shall be my Trust, if you vouchsafe the name, and I will be to you as you shall please to term me."

"My Hope," quod he, "if you so be pleased."

And thus agreed, they two walked apart from the other gentlewoman and fell into sad talk, wherein Mistress Frances did very courteously declare unto him that indeed one cause of her sorrow sustained in his behalf was that he had said so openly overnight that he could not love, for she perceived very well the affection between him and Madam Elynor, and she was also advertised that Dame Elynor stood in the portal of her chamber, harkening to the talk that they had at supper that night, wherefore she seemed to be sorry that such a word—rashly escaped—might become great hindrance unto his desire.

But a greater cause of her grief was, as she declared, that his hap was to bestow his liking so unworthily, for she seemed to accuse Dame Elynor for the most unconstant woman living, in full proof whereof she bewrayed unto F.J. how she the same Dame Elynor had of long time been yielded to the minion secretary, whom I have before described.

"In whom though there be," quod she, "no one point of worthiness, yet shameth she not to use him as her dearest friend, or rather her holiest idol."

And that this notwithstanding, Dame Elynor had been also sundry times won to choice of change,[†] as she named unto F.J. two gentlemen whereof the one was named H.D. and the other H.K., by whom she was during sundry times of their several abode in those parties entreated to like courtesy.

For these causes the Dame Frances seemed to mislike F.J.'s choice and to lament that she doubted in process of time to see him abused. The experiment she meant was this, for that she thought F.J.—I use her words—a man in every respect very worthy to have the several[†] use of a more commodious common, she hoped now to see if his enclosure[†] thereof might be defensible against her said secretary, and such like. These things and divers other of great importance, this courteous Lady Frances did friendly disclose unto F.J. and furthermore did both instruct and advise him how to proceed in his enterprise.

Now to make my talk good, and lest the reader might be drawn in a jealous suppose of this Lady Frances, I must let

---

[†]*choice of change*. The author often used *choice* and *change* within a given context, including poetry associated with his real name:

> *Love then thy choice wherein such* **choice** *thou bind,*
> *As naught but death may ever* **change** *thy mind.*

[†]*every ... very ... several*. a veritable clustering of *ver*-words.

[†]*common ... enclosure*. a contrast of common vs. private use of land, with 'private' relating to 'several', land held in severalty, which was often enclosed; here the contrast is intended as bawdy plays on F.J.'s private use of a common mistress; the passage evinces an analogous and quite stunning overlap with a sonnet the author wrote under his celebrated *Shakespeare* pseudonym, where *fair truth* is used as a pun on Vere truth:

> *Why should my heart think that a* **several** *plot,*
> *Which my heart knows the wide world's* **common** *place?*
> *Or mine eyes, seeing this, say this is not*
> *To put* **fair truth** *upon so foul a face?*
> *Sonnet 137, 9-12.*

you understand that she was unto F.J. a kinswoman, a virgin of rare chastity, singular capacity, notable modesty, and excellent beauty. And though F.J. had cast his affection on the other, being a married woman, yet was there in their beauties no great difference, but in all other good gifts a wonderful diversity, as much as might be between constancy and flitting fantasy, between womanly countenance and girlish garishness, between hot dissimulation and temperate fidelity.

Now if any man will curiously ask the question why F.J. should choose the one and leave the other, over and besides the common proverb—so many men, so many minds—thus may be answered: we see by common experience that the highest flying faucon doth more commonly prey upon the corn-fed crow and the simple shiftless dove than on the mounting kite. And why? Because the one is overcome with less difficulty than that other, thus much in defense of this Lady Frances and to excuse the choice of my friend F.J. who thought himself now no less beholding to good fortune to have found such a trusty friend than bounden to Dame Venus to have won such a mistress.

And to return unto my pretense, understand you that F.J. being now with these two fair ladies come very near the castle grew in some jealous doubt, as on his own behalf, whether he were best to break company or not, when his assured Hope, perceiving the same, 'gan thus recomfort him:

"Good sir," quod she, "if you trusted your trusty friends, you should not need thus cowardly to stand in dread of your friendly enemies."

"Well said in faith," quod F.J. "And I must confess, you were in my bosom before I wist,[†] but yet I have heard said often that in Trust is treason."

[†]*wist.* knew.

"Well spoken for yourself," quod his Hope.

F.J. now remembering that he had but erewhile taken upon him the name of her Trust came home *per misericordiam,*[†] when his Hope, entering the castle gate, caught hold of his lap[†] and half by force led him by the gallery unto his mistress' chamber, whereas after a little dissembling disdain, he was at last by the good help of his Hope, right thankfully received. And for his mistress was now ready to dine, he was therefore for that time arrested there, and *a supersedias*[†] sent into the great chamber unto the Lord of the house, who expected his coming out of the park.

The dinner ended and he thoroughly contented both with welfare and welcome, they fell into sundry devices of pastime. At last F.J. taking into his hand a lute that lay on his mistress' bed did unto the note of the Venetian galliard apply the Italian ditty written by the worthy Bradamant[†] unto the noble Rugier,[†] as Ariosto[†] hath it, *Rugier qual semper fui,*[†] etc. But his mistress could not be quiet until she heard him repeat the tintarnell which he used overnight,[†] the which F.J. refusèd not, at end whereof his mistress thinking now she had showed herself too earnest to use any further dissimulation, especially perceiving the toward inclination of her servant's Hope, fell to flat plain

---

[†]*per misericordiam.* despondent, miserable, sad-hearted.

[†]*lap.* coattail, with possible bawdy play.

[†]*a supersedias.* legal term for suspension of a lord's intent or a stay of legal proceedings.

[†]*Bradamant.* protagonist of Ariosto's epic *Orlando Furioso.*

[†]*Rugier.* beloved of Bradamant in Ariosto's epic.

[†]*Ariosto.* author of the extended narrative poem *Orlando Furioso.*

[†]*Rugier qual semper fui.* line from *Orlando Furioso:* Rugier whose I have always been.

[†]*tintarnell which he used overnight.* possible play on Nell, hence on Elinor, possibly via inter-Nell, with associated wordplay on the **O**xford **Ver**e, via *overnight.*

dealing, and walking to the window, called her servant apart unto her, of whom she demanded secretly and in sad earnest:

"Who devised this tintarnell?"

"My father's sister's brother's son," quod F.J.

His mistress, laughing right heartily, demanded yet again by whom the same was figured.

"By a niece to an aunt of yours, mistress," quod he.

"Well then servant," quod she, "I swear unto you here by my father's soul that my mother's youngest daughter doth love your father's eldest son above any creature living."

F.J. hereby recomforted 'gan thus reply: "Mistress, though my father's eldest son be far unworthy of so noble a match, yet since it pleaseth her so well to accept him, I would thus much say behind his back that your mother's daughter hath done him some wrong."

"And wherein servant?" quod she.

"By my troth, Mistress," quod he, "it is not yet twenty hours since without touch of breast she gave him such a nip by the heart as did altogether bereave him his night's rest with the bruise thereof."

"Well, servant," quod she, "content yourself, and for your sake, I will speak to her to provide him a plaster, the which I myself will apply to his hurt. And to the end it may work the better with him, I will purvey a lodging for him, where hereafter he may sleep at more quiet."

This said, the rosy hue distrained her sickly cheeks and she returned to the company, leaving F.J. ravished between hope and dread,[†] as one that could neither conjecture the

---

[†]*between* hope *and* dread. again reminiscent of the author's diction within the Shakespeare opus, as in *The Rape of Lucrece:*

And now this lustful lord leaped from his bed,

...

Is madly tossed **between** *desire* **and dread:**

42

meaning of her mystical words, nor assuredly trust unto the knot of her sliding affections, when the Lady Frances, coming to him, demanded:

"What? Dream you sir?"

"Yea marry do I, fair lady," quod he.

"And what was your dream, Sir?" quod she.

"I dreamt," quod F.J., "that walking in a pleasant garden garnished with sundry delights, my hap was to espy hanging in the air a hope wherein I might well behold the aspects and face of the heavens, and calling to remembrance the day and hour of my nativity, I did thereby, according to my small skill in astronomy, try the conclusions of mine adventures."

"And what found you therein?" quod Dame Frances.

"You awaked me out of my dream," quod he, "or else, peradventure, you should not have known."

"I believe you well," quod the Lady Frances, and laughing at his quick answer, brought him by the hand unto the rest of his company, where he tarried not long before his gracious mistress bad him to farewell and to keep his hour there again when he should by her be summoned. Hereby F.J. passed the rest of that day in hope, awaiting the happy time when his mistress should send for him.

Suppertime came and passed over and not long after came the handmaid of the Lady Elynor into the great chamber, desiring F.J. to repair unto their mistress, the which he willingly accomplished. And being now entered into her chamber, he might perceive his mistress in her night's attire, preparing herself towards bed, to whom F.J. said: "Why how now mistress? I had thought this night to have seen you dance—at least or at last—amongst us?"

"By my troth, good servant," quod she. "I adventured so soon unto the great chamber yesternight that I find myself somewhat sickly disposed and therefore do strain courtesy, as you see, to go the sooner to my bed this night. But before I sleep," quod she, "I am to charge you with a matter of weight."

And taking him apart from the rest, declared that—as that present night—she would talk with him more at large in the gallery near adjoining to her chamber.

Hereupon F.J. discretely dissembling his joy, took his leave and returned into the great chamber where he had not long continued before the Lord of the castle commanded a torch to light him unto his lodging, whereas he prepared himself and went to bed, commanding his servant also to go to his rest. And when he thought as well his servant as the rest of household to be safe, he arose again, and taking his nightgown, did under the same convey his naked sword[†] and so walked to the gallery where he found his good mistress walking in her nightgown and attending his coming.[†]

The moon was now at the full, the skies clear, and the weather temperate, by reason whereof he might the more plainly and with the greater contentation behold his long desired joys. And spreading his arms abroad to embrace his loving mistress, he said: "Oh my dear lady, when shall I be able with any desert to countervail[†] the least part of this your bountiful goodness?"

The dame, whether it were of fear in deed, or that the wiliness of womanhood had taught her to cover her conceits with some fine dissimulation, stert[†] back from the knight and shrieking—but softly—said unto him:

[†]*naked sword.* obvious phallic reference; cf. appended essay.
[†]*attending his coming.* with sexual innuendo.
[†]*countervail.* along with the preceding **contentation**, a plausible quibble on the female pudendum.
[†]*stert.* started.

"Alas servant, what have I deserved that you come a-gainst me with naked sword as against an open† enemy?"

F.J. perceiving her intent excused himself, declaring that he brought the same for their defense and not to offend her in any wise. The lady being therewith somewhat appeased, they began with more comfortable gesture to expel the dread of the said late affright and sithens to become bolder of behavior, more familiar in speech, and most kind in accomplishing of common comfort.

But why hold I so long discourse in describing the joys which—for lack of like experience—I cannot set out to the full? Were it not that I know to whom I write, I would the more beware what I write. F.J. was a man, and neither of us are senseless. And therefore I should slander him—over and besides a greater obloquy to the whole genealogy of Eneas†—if I should imagine that of tender heart he would forbear to express her more tender limbs against the hard floor.

Sufficed that of her courteous nature she was content to accept boards for a bed of down, mats for cameric sheets, and the nightgown of F.J. for a counterpoint to cover† them, and thus with calm content instead of quiet sleep, they beguiled the night† until she, proudest star, began to abandon the firmament, when F.J. and his mistress were constrained also to abandon their delights and with ten thousand sweet

---

†*open.* play on Elinor's readiness to receive F.J.; the sex act was not uncommonly expressed metaphorically as war or battle, as remarked in an earlier note, hence the *open enemy.*

†*the whole genealogy of Eneas.* all Englishmen, i.e. traditionally considered of the line of Brutus, legendary great-grandson of the Trojan Eneas (= Aeneas), the subject of Virgil's Latin epic.

†*counterpoint to cover them.* phallic innuendo with *cover* serving as an added play on both coitus and the **Oxford Vere.**

†*beguiled the night.* the *time-beguiling sport* evinced by the author later in *Venus and Adonis* under the *Shakespeare* pseudonym.

kisses and straight embracings did frame themselves to play loath to depart.

Well, remedy was there none, but Dame Elynor must return unto her chamber and F.J. must also convey himself—as closely† as might be—into his chamber, the which was hard to do, the day being so far sprung and he having a large base court† to pass over before he could recover his stairfoot door. And though he were not much perceived, yet the Lady Frances, being no less desirous to see an issue of these enterprises than F.J. was willing to cover them in secrecy, did watch and even at the entering of his chamber door perceived the point of his naked sword glistering under the skirt of his nightgown, whereat she smiled and said to herself: "This gear goeth well about."†

Well, F.J. having now recovered his chamber, he went to bed and there let him sleep, as his mistress did on that other side. Although the Lady Frances being thoroughly tickled now in all the veins could not enjoy such quiet rest, but arising took another gentlewoman of the house with her and walked into the park to take the fresh air of the morning. They had not long walked there, but they returned and though F.J. had not yet slept sufficiently, for one which had so far travailed in the night past, yet they went into his chamber to raise him, and coming to his bedside, found him fast asleep.

"Alas," quod that other gentlewoman, "it were pity to awake him."

"Even so it were," quod Dame Frances, "but we will take away somewhat of his, whereby he may perceive that we were here."

---

†*closely.* inconspicuously, furtively.
†*base.* lower.
†*This gear goeth well about.* The man is well-pointed; with bawdy play intended.

And looking about the chamber, his naked sword presented itself to the hands of Dame Frances, who took it with her, and softly shutting his chamber door again, went down the stairs and recovered her own lodging in good order and unperceived by anybody, saving only that other gentlewoman which accompanied her.

At the last F.J. awaked and appareling himself walked out also to take the air. And being thoroughly recomforted as well with remembrance of his joys forepassed, as also with the pleasant harmony which the birds made on every tree and the fragrant smell of the redolent flowers and blossoms which budded on every branch, he did in these delights compile these verses following.

The occasion—as I have heard him rehearse—was by encounter that he had with his lady by light of the moon. And forasmuch as the moon in midst of their delights did vanish away, or was overspread with a cloud, thereupon he took the subject of his theme. And thus it ensueth, called 'A Moonshine Banquet'.

G.T.

Dame Cynthia[†] herself, that shines so bright,
   And deigneth not to leave her lofty place:
   But only then when Phoebus shows his face
Which is her brother born and lends her light,
   Disdained not yet to do my lady right:
      To prove that in such heavenly wights as she,
      It sitteth best that right and reason be.
For when she spied my lady's golden rays,
   Into the clouds,
   Her head she shrouds,

---

†**Cynthia ... shines ... shame**. The triad found in this poem is reminiscent of Shakespeare in *Venus and Adonis*: **Cynthia** *for* **shame** *obscures her silver* **shine**. We may add the additional pair *heavenly-heaven*.

And shamed to shine where she her beams displays.
Good reason yet that to my simple skill,
   I should the name of Cynthia adore:
   By whose high help, I might behold the more
My lady's lovely looks at mine own will,[†]
With deep content to gare[†] *and gaze my fill:*
   Of courtesy and not of dark disdain,
   Dame Cynthia disclosed my lady plain.
She did but lend her light, as for a lyte,[†]
   With friendly grace,
   To show her face,
That else would show and shine in her despite.

Dan Phoebus he with many a louring[†] *look,*
   Had her beheld of yore in angry wise:
   And when he could none other mean devise
To stain her name, this deep deceit he took
To be the bait that best might hide his hook:
   Into her eyes his parching beams he cast,
   To scorch their skins that gazed on her full fast:
Whereby when many a man was sun burnt so
   They thought my Queen,[†]
   The sun had been
With scalding flames, which wrought them all that woe.

[†]*will.* another example of the author's play on his willy, for which see the essay following the novel.

[†]*gare.* gape, stare; also spelled *gaure.*

[†]*lyte.* mental illumination or elucidation; an eye. Here **light**, *as for* **lyte** is reminiscent of Shakespeare's play on two senses of *light* in *Love's Labor's Lost 2.1:* **light** *in the* **light**, with similar play in Act 5 touching on the bawdy sense 'loose', which may also be intended here.

[†]*louring.* staring; a more likely normalization than *lowering,* although the latter has been favored by some scholars influenced by spelling.

[†]*my Queen.* a clue bearing on the claim that Elinor is a figuration of England's Queen; cf. discussion in the following essay.

And thus when many a look had looked so long,
　As that their eyes were dim and dazzled both:
　Some fainting hearts that were both lewd and loath
　To look again from whence the error sprong,
　Gan close their eye for fear of further wrong:
　And some again once drawn into the maze,
　Gan lewdly blame the beams of beauty's blaze:
But I with deep foresight did soon espy,
　How Phoebus meant,
　By false intent,
To slander so her name with cruelty.

Wherefore at better leisure thought I best,†
　To try the treason of his treachery:
　And to exalt my lady's dignity
When Phoebus fled and drew him down to rest
Amid the waves that walter† in the West.
　I 'gan behold this lovely lady's face,
　Whereon Dame Nature spent her gifts of grace:
And found therein no parching heat at all,
　But such bright hue,
　As might renew,
An angel's joys in reign celestial.

The courteous Moon that wished to do me good,
　Did shine to show my dame more perfectly,
　But when she saw her passing jollity,
The Moon for shame did blush as red as blood,
And shrunk aside and kept her horns in hood:
　So that now when Dame Cynthia was gone,
　I might enjoy my lady's looks alone,

---

†**better** ... **best**. The *better-best* contrast is rife throughout the Shake-speare opus, a representative example of which is drawn from *Sonnet 91: All these I **better** in one general **best**.*
†*walter*. roll.

Yet honored still the Moon with true intent:
Who taught us skill,
To work our will,[†]
And gave us place till all the night was spent.
F. J.

This ballad—or howsoever I[†] shall term it—percase you will not like, and yet in my judgment it hath great good store of deep invention. And for the order of the verse, it is not common. I have not heard many of like proportion. Some will account it but a diddledum, but who so had heard F.J. sing it to the lute by a note of his own devise, I suppose he would esteem it to be a pleasant diddledum. And for my part, if I were not partial I would say more in commendation of it than now I mean to do, leaving it to your and like judgments.

And now to return to my tale, by that time that F.J. returned out of the park, it was dinnertime, and at dinner they all met—I mean both Dame Elynor, Dame Frances, and F.J. I leave to describe that the Lady Frances was gorgeously attired and set forth with very brave apparel and Madam Elynor only in her nightgown girt to her, with a coif trimmed *alla Piedmontese*[†] on the which she ware[†] a little cap crossed over[†] the crown with two bands of

---

[†]*work our will.* bawdy.

[†]*howsoever I.* with a covert reading *E. Ver I,* as throughout the novel.

[†]*alla Piedmontese.* play on the *mons pubis* via *Pied-monte,* 'foot of the mountain', as confirmed in the next footnotes.

[†]*ware.* overtly, past tense of *wear;* covertly, a not uncommon codeword for genitalia.

[†]*cap crossed over.* a likely play on genitalia, as indicated by (*i*) the conjunction of *Piedmontese* and *ware* of the last two notes, (*ii*) the following word *Contented,* and (*iii*) convergence with Shakespeare as indicated in the next footnote. Hyphenation wordplay inheres in the original text as *o/ver*, with a play on the **O**xford **Ver**e and a possible bawdy play on *o*, as amplified in Chapter 0 of *Shakespeare's Fingerprints*.

yellow† sarcenet† or cypress, in the midst whereof she had placed—of her own handwriting—in paper this word, *Contented.*†

This attire pleased her then to use and could not have displeased Mistress Frances had she not been more privy to the cause than to the thing itself. At least the Lord of the castle of ignorance and Dame Frances of great temperance let it pass without offense.

At dinner, because the one was pleased with all former reckonings and the other made privy to the account, there passed no word of taunt or grudge, but *omnia bene.*† After dinner Dame Elinor being no less desirous to have F.J.'s company than Dame Frances was to take him on some pretty trip, they began to question how they might best pass the day.

The Lady Elynor seemed desirous to keep her chamber, but Mistress Frances for another purpose seemed desirous to ride abroad thereby to take the open air. They agreed to ride a mile or twain for solace and requested F.J. to accompany them, the which willingly granted, each one parted from other to prepare themselves and now began the sport, for when F.J. was booted, his horses saddled, and he ready to ride, he 'gan miss his rapier, whereat all astonied, he began to blame his man, but blame whom he would, found it could not be.

At last the ladies going towards horseback called for him in the base court and demanded if he were ready, to whom F.J. answered: "Madams, I am more than ready and yet not so ready as I would be."

---

†*crossed ... yellow.* suggestive of infidelity, as also under the *Shakespeare* pseudonym with respect to the conjunction of *yellow* stockings and *cross-gartered* in *Twelfth Night.*
†*sarcenet.* very fine soft silk; also spelled *sarsenet.*
†*Contented.* pun on the pudendum, consistent with the last footnotes.
†*omnia bene.* all's well.

And immediately taking himself in trip, he thought best to utter no more of his conceit, but in haste more than good speed, mounted his horse and coming toward the dames, presented himself, turning, bounding, and taking up his courser to the uttermost of his power in bravery.

After suffering his horse to breathe himself, he 'gan also allay his own choler and to the dames he said: "Fair ladies, I am ready when it pleaseth you to ride where so you command."

"Now ready soever you[†] be, servant," quod Dame Elinor. "It seemeth your horse is readier at your command than at ours."

"If he be at my command, Mistress," quod he, "he shall be at yours."

"Gramercy, good servant," quod she, "but my meaning is that I fear he be too stirring for our company."

"If he prove so, mistress," quod F.J., "I have here a soberer palfrey to serve you on."[†]

The dames being mounted, they rode forthwards by the space of a mile or very near, and F.J.—whether it were of his horse's courage[†] or his own choler—came not so near them as they wished.

At last the Lady Frances said unto him: "Master J., you said that you had a soberer horse, which if it be so, we would be glad of your company, but I believe by your countenance, your horse and you are agreed."

[†]*soever you. ver*-wordplay; *s(eventeenth)o(xford)e(dward)ver* = **soever**.

[†]*palfrey to serve you on.* a bawdy reference to Freeman's pudendum, consistent with the appearance of *courage* below, as is the horse itself.

[†]*courage.* Consonant with the preceding note and with the following is Madelon Gohlke's observation: "'Courage' or 'corage' is a pun ... referring as it does in the Renaissance both to military prowess and to sexual desire." Within the Spenserian context, Gohlke [1978:136, fn. 16] asserts: "The rousing of Guyon's 'courage cold,' I would argue, constitutes a not very veiled allusion to an erection."

F.J. alighting called his servant, changed horses with him, and overtaking the dames said to Mistress Frances: "And why do you think, fair lady, that my horse and I are agreed?"[†]

"Because by your countenance," quod she, "it seemeth your patience is stirred."

"In good faith," quod F.J., "you have guessed aright, but not with any of you."

"Then we care the less, servant," quod Dame Elinor.

"By my troth mistress," quod F.J.—looking well about him that none might hear but they two—"it is with my servant, who hath lost my sword out of my chamber."

Dame Elinor, little remembering the occasion, replied: "It is no matter servant," quod she. "You shall hear of it again I warrant you, and presently we ride in God's peace and I trust shall have no need of it."

"Yet mistress," quod he, "a weapon serveth both uses, as well to defend, as to offend."[†]

"Now by my troth," quod Dame Frances, "I have now my dream, for I dreamt this night that I was in a pleasant meadow alone, where I met with a tall gentleman appareled in a nightgown of silk, all embroidered about with a guard of naked swords. And when he came towards me, I seemed to be afraid of him.

"But he recomforted me saying: 'Be not afraid fair lady, for I use this garment only for mine own defense.' And in this sort went that warlike god, Mars, what time he taught Dame Venus to make Vulcan a hammer of the new fash-

---

[†]*my horse and I are agreed.* Pigman [2001] notes: "F.J.'s inability to manage his horse is a time-honoured trope for his inability to restrain his sexual desire", citing Bartlett Giamatti's 'Headlong Horses, Headless Horsemen: An Essay on the Chivalric Epics of Pulci, Boiardo, and Ariosto', published in *Italian Literature, Roots and Branches: Essays in Honor of Thomas Goddard Bergin.*

[†]*two uses ... offend.* a bawdy play on F.J.'s weapon.

ion.[†] Notwithstanding these comfortable words, the fright of the dream awaked me and sithens unto this hour I have not slept at all."

"And what time of the night dreamt you this?" quod F.J.

"In the gray morning, about dawning of the day. But why ask you?" quod Dame Frances.

F.J. with a great sigh answered: "Because that dreams are to be marked[†] more at some hour of the night than at some other."

"Why are you so cunning[†] at the interpretation of dreams, servant?" quod the Lady Elynor.

"Not very cunning Mistress," quod F.J., "but guess, like a young scholar."

The dames continued in these and like pleasant talks, but F.J. could not be merry, as one that esteemed the preservation of his mistress' honor no less than the obtaining of his own delights. And yet to avoid further suspicion, he repressed his passions as much as he could.

The Lady Elynor more careless than considerative of her own case,[†] pricking forwards, said softly to F.J.: "I had thought you had received small cause, servant, to be thus dumpish, when I would be merry."[†]

"Alas, dear mistress," quod F.J., "it is altogether for your sake that I am pensive."

[†]*a hammer of the new fashion.* Mars lay with Vulcan's wife Venus; hence the hammer of new fashion suggests cuckoldry.

[†]*marked.* with possible bawdy significance, as in the Shakespeare opus, e.g. *Love's Labour's Lost 4.1: Let the mark have a prick in't.*

[†]*cunning.* compare previous note and subsequent use of both *not* and *cunning* in the phrase *not very cunning.*

[†]*her own case.* play on the female pudendum, suggested by the ensuing word *pricking* and its appearance elsewhere, e.g. *Eastward Ho 3.2: I have seen a little prick no bigger than a pin's head swell bigger and bigger, till it has come to an ancome; and e'en so't is in these **cases**.*

[†]*merry.* often used in the bawdy spirit of 'naughty'.

Dame Frances with courtesy withdrew herself and gave them leave, whenas F.J. declared unto his mistress that his sword was taken out of his chamber and that he dreaded much by the words of the Lady Frances that she had some understanding of the matter.

Dame Elynor, now calling to remembrance what had passed the same night, at the first was abashed, but immediately, for these women be readily witted, cheered her servant and willed him to commit unto her the salving of that sore.[†] Thus they passed the rest of the way in pleasant talk with Dame Frances and so returned towards the castle where F.J. suffered the two dames to go together and he alone unto his chamber to bewail his own misgovernment. But Dame Elynor, whether it were according to old custom or by wily policy, found mean[†] that night that the sword was conveyed out of Mistress Frances' chamber and brought unto hers, and after redelivery of it unto F.J., she warned him to be more wary from that time forthwards.

Well, I dwell too long upon these particular points in discoursing this trifling history, but that the same is the more apt mean of introduction to the verses, which I mean to rehearse unto you, and I think you will not disdain to read my conceit with his invention about declaration of his comedy. The next that ever F.J.[†] wrote then, upon any adventure happened between him and this fair lady, was this, as I have heard him say, and upon this occasion: after he grew more bold and better acquainted with his mistress' disposition, he adventured one Friday in the morning to go unto her chamber and thereupon wrote as followeth, which he termed a Friday's Breakfast.

G. T.

[†]*that sore.* bawdy, i.e. Elinor's pudendum.
[†]*mean.* a means.
[†]*ever F.J.* whence E. Vere = F.J.

That selfsame day, and of that day that hour,
When she doth reign, that mocked Vulcan the Smith:†
And thought it meet to harbor in her bower,
Some gallant guest for her to dally with.

That blessèd hour, that blisst and happy day,
I thought it meet with hasty steps to go
Unto the lodge, wherein my lady lay,
To laugh for joy or else to weep for woe.

And lo, my lady of her wonted grace,
First lent her lips to me as for a kiss:
And after that her body to embrace,
Wherein Dame Nature wrought nothing amiss.

What followed next, guess you that know the trade,
For in this sort, my Friday's feast I made.
                    F. J.

This sonnet is short and sweet, reasonably well, according to the occasion, &c. Many days passed these two lovers with great delight, their affairs being no less politicly governed than happily achieved. And surely I have heard F.J. affirm in sad earnest that he did not only love her, but was furthermore so ravished in ecstasy with continual remembrance of his delights that he made an idol of her in his inward concept. So seemeth it by this challenge to beauty, which he wrote in her praise and upon her name.
                    G. T.

---

†*that mocked Vulcan the smith.* Venus, who mocked her husband by her affair with Mars; hence, the title *Friday's Breakfast*, as Friday was Venus' day.

ADVENTURES OF FREEMAN JONES

Beauty shut up thy shop and truss up all thy trash,
My Nell[†] hath stolen thy finest stuff and left thee in the lash:[†]
Thy market now is marred, thy gains are gone God wot,[†]
Thou hast no ware[†] that may compare with this that I have got.
As for thy painted pale and wrinkles surfled up[†]
Are dear enough for such as lust to drink of every cup.
Thy bodies bolstered out, with bombast and with bags,
Thy rolls, thy ruffs, thy cowls, thy coifs, thy jerkins and thy jags.
Thy curling and thy cost, thy frizzling and thy fare,
To court to court with all those toys and there set forth such ware
Before their hungry eyes, that gaze on every guest,
And choose the cheapest chaffer still to please their fancy best.
But I whose steadfast eyes could never cast a glance,
With wand'ring look amid the prease[†] to take my choice by chance
Have won by due desert a piece[†] that hath no peer,
And left the rest as refuse all to serve the market there.
There let him choose that list, there catch the best who can.
A painted blazing bait may serve to choke a gazing man.
But I have slipped thy flower,[†] that freshest is of hue;
I have thy corn, go sell thy chaff,[†] I list to seek no new.
The windows of mine eyes are glazed with such delight,
As each new face seems full of faults that blazeth in my sight;

[†]*Nell.* nickname for Elinor, and possibly Elizabeth, cf. appended essay.
[†]*lash.* lurch.
[†]*wot.* knows.
[†]*ware.* female pudendum, as remarked in an earlier note.
[†]*surfled up.* hidden with makeup.
[†]*prease.* throng.
[†]*piece.* a woman conceived of sexually.
[†]*slipped thy flower.* deflowered.
[†]**corn, go sell ... chaff.** These words show up in a line of a poem appearing under the *Whetstone* pseudonym, along with additional impressive overlap of *n*-tuples across the two poems: *Then **go** and market keep where **chaff** is **sold** for **corn**.* Elaboration and discussion of the two poems will be found in *Never and For Ever.* Independent evidence that *Whetstone* is a pseudonym for our author is provided in Chapter 14 of *Shakespeare's Fingerprints.*

And not without just cause, I can compare her so,
Lo here my glove I challenge him[†] that can or dare say no.
Let Theseus come with club, or Paris brag with brand,
To prove how fair their Helen was that scourged the Grecian land:
Let mighty Mars himself come armèd to the field,
And vaunt Dame Venus to defend with helmet, spear, and shield.
This hand that had good hap, my Helen to embrace,
Shall have like luck to foil her foes and daunt them with disgrace,
And cause them to confess by verdict and by oath,
How far her lovely looks do stain[†] the beauties of them both,
And that my Helen[†] is more fair than Paris' wife,
And doth deserve more famous praise than Venus for her life,
Which if I not perform, my life then let me lease,
Or else be bound in chains of change to beg for beauty's fees.
                                        F. J.

By this challenge I guess that either he was then in an ecstasy, or else sure I am now, in a lunacy, for it is a proud challenge made to Beauty herself and all her companions. And imagining that Beauty having a shop where she uttered her wares of all sundry sorts, his lady had stolen the finest away, leaving none behind her but painting, bolstering, forcing and suchlike, the which in his rage he judgeth good enough to serve the Court,[†] and thereupon grew a great quarrel. When these verses[†] were by the negligence of his mistress dispersed into sundry hands, and so at last to the reading of a courtier—well, F.J. had his desire if his mistress liked them, but as I have heard him declare, she grew

---

[†]*I challenge him.* Compare the Whetstone line in the poem noted in the last footnote: *And him I challenge forth by force of fight to prove.*
[†]*stain.* so excel as to stain.
[†]*Helen.* comparing Elinor with Helen of Troy, who forsook her husband for Paris.
[†]*Court.* a likely reference to the Tudor Court, as also the reference to *courtier;* cf. Section 3 of the accompanying essay.
[†]*verses.* play on *Vere,* a hyphenation print in original as *ver/ses.*

58

in jealousy that the same were not written by her,[†] because her name was Elynor and not Helen.[†]

And about this point have been divers[†] and sundry opinions, for this and divers other of his most notable poems have come to view of the world, although altogether without his consent. And some have attributed this praise unto a Helen who deserved not so well as this Dame Elynor should seem to deserve by the relation of F.J. and yet never a barrel of good herring between them both.[†] But that other Helen, because she was and is of so base condition, as may deserve no manner commendation in any honest judgment, therefore I will excuse my friend F.J. and adventure my pen in his behalf, that he would never bestow verse of so mean a subject. And yet some of his acquaintance, being also acquainted, better than I, that F.J. was sometimes acquainted with Helen, have stood in argument with me that it was written by Helen and not by Elynor.[†]

Well F.J. told me himself that it was written by this Dame Elynor and that unto her he thus alleged that he took it all for one name, or at least he never read of any Elinor such matter as might sound worthy like commendation for beauty. And indeed, considering that it was in the first beginning of his writings, as then he was no writer of any long continuance comparing also the time that such reports do spread of his acquaintance with Helen, it cannot be written less than six or seven years before he knew Helen.

[†]*by her.* about her; and repeatedly in the ensuing text.

[†]*Helen.* original spelling with double *l* as *Hellen,* which should perhaps be retained if intended to relate to Nell (reversal of the terminal segment of *Hellen* yields *Nell);* single *l* in *Elinor* motivates our choice of modern *Helen.*

[†]*divers.* play on *de Vere* via a left margination print in the original text.

[†]*never ... them both.* nothing to choose between them; they are alike.

[†]*by Helen and not by Elynor.* about Helen and not about Elynor.

Marry, peradventure if there were any acquaintance between F.J. and that Helen afterwards—the which I dare not confess—he might adapt it to her name and so make it serve both their turns, as elder lovers have done before and still do and will to world without end.[†] Amen.

Well, by whom he wrote it I know not, but once[†] I am sure that he wrote it, for he is no borrower of inventions and this is all that I mean to prove, as one that send you his verses by stealth and do him double wrong to disclose unto any man the secret causes why they were devised. But this for your delight I do adventure.

And to return to the purpose, he sought more certainly to please his mistress Elynor with this sonnet written in her praise as followeth.

G. T.

The stately dames of Rome, their pearls did wear,[†]
About their necks to beautify their name:
But she, whom I do serve, her pearls doth bear,
Close in her mouth and smiling shows the same.

No wonder then though[†] *every word she speaks,*
A jewel seems in judgment of the wise,
Since that her sugared tongue the passage breaks,
Between two rocks, bedecked with pearls of prize.

[†]**world without end**. as in *Love's Labor's Lost 5.2* and *Sonnet 57:*
   A time, methinks, too short to make a **world without end** *bargain in.*
   Nor dare I chide the **world without end** *hour.*
[†]*once*. of one thing.
[†]*The stately dames of Rome ... wear.* Pigman [2000:580] claims that the author Whetstone plays with this line in his *Heptameron,* while it is shown in Chapter 14 of *Shakespeare Fingerprints* that the latter work is to be attributed to the author of *Flowers,* namely Edward de Vere, 17th Earl of Oxford, thereby providing explanations where orthodoxy offers descriptions or observations.
[†]*No wonder* **then though**. evincing more overlap with Shakespeare, e.g. with line 5 of *Sonnet 44:* **No matter *then although*** *my foot did stand.*

ADVENTURES OF FREEMAN JONES

Her hair of gold, her front of ivory,
A bloody heart within so white a breast,
Her teeth of pearl, lips ruby, crystal eye,
Needs must I honor her above the rest:

Since she is formèd of none other mould,
But ruby, crystal, ivory, pearl, and gold.
F. J.

Of this sonnet I am assured that it is but a translation, for
I myself have seen the invention of an Italian, and Master J.
hath a little dilated the same, but not much besides the
sense of the first and the addition very aptly applied,[†]
wherefore I cannot condemn his doing therein. And for the
sonnet, were it not a little too much praise—as the Italians
do most commonly offend in the superlative—I could the
more commend it, but I hope the party to whom it was dedicated had rather it were much more than anything less.

Well, thus these two lovers passed many days in exceeding contentation[†] and more than speakable pleasures, in
which time F.J. did compile very many verses according to
sundry occasions proffered,[†] whereof I have not obtained
the most at his hands and the reason that he deemed me the
same was that—as he alleged—they were for the most part
soured with a taste of glory.[†] As you know that in such
cases[†] a lover being charged with inexprivable[†] joys, and

---

[†]*very aptly applied.* i.e. aptly applied in Vere fashion; *very* hyphenated
in the original to enhance wordplay recognition.
[†]*contentation.* with a plausibly bawdy reading.
[†]*very many verses ... proffered.* with multiple quibbles on the author's
name *Vere,* including *proffered*, with hyphenation of *very* in the original as *ve/ry* to aid recognition of intended wordplay.
[†]*glory.* See the appended essay for possible wordplay.
[†]*cases.* a likely play on female pudenda.
[†]*inexprivable.* inexpressible.

therewith enjoined both by duty and discretion to keep the same covert, can by no means devise a greater consolation than to commit it into some ciphered[†] words and figured speeches in verse, whereby he feeleth his heart half—or more than half—eased of swelling. For as sighs are some present ease to the pensive mind, even so we find by experience that such secret intercommoning[†] of joys doth increase delight. I would not have you conster[†] my words to this effect, that I think a man cannot sufficiently rejoice in the lucky lots of love, unless he impart the same to others.

God forbid that ever I[†] should enter into such a heresy, for I have always been of this opinion, that as to be fortunate in love is one of the most inward contentations to man's mind of all earthly joys. Even so, if he do but once bewray the same to any living creature, immediately either dread of discovering doth bruise his breast with an intolerable burden or else he leaseth the principal virtue which gave effect to his gladness, not unlike to a 'pothecary's pot which being filled with sweet ointments or perfumes doth retain in itself some scent of the same, and being poured out doth return to the former state: hard, harsh, and of small savor. So the mind being fraught with delights, as long as it can keep them secretly enclosed, may continually feed upon the pleasant record thereof as the well willing and ready horse biteth on the bridle. But having once disclosed them to any other, straightway we lose the hidden treasure of the same and are oppressed with sundry doubtful opinions and dreadful conceits. And yet for a man to record unto himself in the inward contemplation of his mind, the often remem-

---

[†]*ciphered.* "ciphered words" in "verse" being descriptive of the author's very practice throughout, with the preceding word *covert* a play on the **O**xford **Ve**re, as also the spate of *ver*-words following.
[†]*intercommoning.* sharing.
[†]*conster.* construe.
[†]*ever I.* wordplay pointing to E. Vere = I; see the essay following.

brance of his late receivèd joys doth, as it were, ease the heart of burden and add unto the mind a fresh supply of delight.

Yea, and in verse principally—as I conceive—a man may best contrive this way of comfort in himself. Therefore as I have said, F.J. swimming now in delights did nothing but write such verse as might accumulate his joys to the extremity of pleasure, the which for that purpose he kept from me, as one more desirous to seem obscure and defective than overmuch to glory in his adventures, especially for that in the end his hap was as heavy as hitherto he had been fortunate.

Amongst other I remembered one happened upon this occasion. The husband of the Lady Elynor, being all this while absent from her, 'gan now return and kept cut at home, with whom F.J. found means so to insinuate himself that familiarity took deep root between them and seldom but by stealth you could find the one out of the other's company. On a time the knight riding on hunting desired F.J. to accompany him, the which he could not refuse to do, but like a lusty yonker,[†] ready at all assays, appareled himself in green and about his neck a bugle, pricking[†] and galloping amongst the foremost, according to the manner of that country.

And it chanced that the married knight thus galloping lost his horn,[†] which some divines might have interpreted to be but molting and that, by God's grace, he might have anew come up again shortly instead of that. Well, he came to F.J., requiring him to lend him his bugle, for—said the knight:

---

†*yonker.* gay, fashionable youth.
†*pricking.* another example of penis play.
†*lost his horn.* a reference to cuckoldry, as in the following poem.

"I heard you not blow this day and I would fain encourage the hounds, if I had a horn."

Quod F.J.: "Although I have not been over-lavish of my coming[†] hitherto, I would you should not doubt but that I can tell how to use a horn well enough, and yet I may little do if I may not lend you a horn," and therewithal took his bugle from his neck and lent it to the knight, who making in unto the hounds, 'gan assay to rechate.[†] But the horn was too hard for him to wind, whereat F.J. took pleasure and said to himself:

"Blow till thou break that. I made thee one within these few days that thou wilt never crack whiles thou livest," and hereupon—before the fall of the buck[†]—devised this sonnet following, which at his homecoming he presented unto his mistress.

G. T.

As some men say there is a kind of seed
Will grow to horns if it be sowèd thick:
Wherewith I thought to try if I could breed
A brood of buds, well sharpèd in the prick:

And by good proof of learnèd skill I found,
As on some special soil all seeds best frame,

[†]*my coming.* bawdily, in light of what follows.

[†]*assay to rechate.* try to blow the horn (literally to regroup the hounds); the paragraph is replete with wanton wordplay.

[†]*the fall of the buck.* an intimation of cuckoldry reminiscent of Shakespeare's *Merry Wives of Windsor* where Ford, fearful of being cuckolded, exclaims: *Buck? I would I could wash myself of the buck!* Tilley [1950: W699] cites a lovely example from 1658 in which the name *Buckingame* clearly intimates cuckoldry:

Women are borne in Wilshire, Brought up in Cumberland, Lead
their lives in Bedfordshire, Bring their husbands to Buckingame,
And die in Shrewsbury.

So jealous brains do breed the battleground,
That best of all might serve to bear the same.

Then sought I forth to find such supple soil,
And called to mind thy husband had a brain,
So that percase, by travail and by toil,
His fruitful front might turn my seed to gain:

And as I gropèd in that ground to sow it,
Start up a horn, thy husband could not blow it.
F. J.

This sonnet treateth of a strange seed, but it tasteth most of rye, which is more common amongst men nowadays. Well, let it pass amongst the rest and he that liketh it not, turn over the leaf to another. I doubt not but in this register he may find some to content him, unless he be too curious and here I will surcease to rehearse any more of his verses, until I have expressed how that his joys being now exalted to the highest degree, began to bend towards declination. For now the unhappy secretary whom I have before remembered was returned from London, on whom F.J. had no sooner cast his eyes, but immediately he fell into a great passion of mind, which might be compared unto a fever. This fruit grew of the good instructions that his Hope had planted in his mind, whereby I might take just occasion to forewarn every lover, how they suffer this venomous serpent jealousy to creep into their conceits. For surely, of all other diseases in love I suppose that to be uncurable and would hold longer discourse therein were it not that both this tale and the verses of F.J. himself hereafter to be recited shall be sufficient to speak for me in this behalf.

The lover, as I say, upon the sudden[†] was drawn into such a malady as no meat might nourish his body, no delights please his mind, no remembrance of joys forepassed content him, nor any hope of the like to come might recomfort him. Hereat some unto whom I have imparted this tale have taken occasion to discommend his fainting heart, yet surely the cause inwardly and deeply considered, I cannot so lightly condemn him. For an old saying is that every man[†] can give counsel better than follow it, and needs must the conflicts of his thoughts be strange between the remembrance of his forepassed pleasure and the present sight of this monster whom before, for lack of like instruction, he had not so thoroughly marked[†] and beheld.

Well, such was the grief unto him that he became sickly and kept his chamber. The ladies having received the news thereof 'gan all at once[†] lament his misfortune and of common consent agreed to visit him. They marched thither in good equipage, I warrant you, and found F.J. lying upon his bed languishing, whom they all saluted generally and sought to recomfort, but especially his mistress, having in her hand a branch of willow,[†] wherewith she defended her from the hot air, 'gan thus say unto him:

"Servant," quod she, "for that I suppose your malady to proceed of none other cause but only slothfulness, I have brought this pretty rod to beat you a little, nothing doubting but when you feel the smart of a twig or twain, you will like a tractable young scholar pluck up your quickened spirits and cast this drowsiness apart."

[†]*upon the sudden.* all of a sudden.

[†]*every man.* i.e. E. Vere man; cf. authorship essay following.

[†]*marked.* cf. *mark* in the appended essay.

[†]*at once.* together.

[†]*willow.* a token of sadness with possible presage of death, reappearing later in the text; cf. willow tree relating to Ophelia's death in *Hamlet* and willow song auguring Desdemona's death in *Othello*.

F.J. with a great sigh answered: "Alas good mistress," quod he, "if any like chastisement might quicken me, how much more might the presence of all you lovely dames recomfort my dullèd mind whom to behold were sufficient to revive an eye now dazzled with the dread of death, and that not only for the heavenly aspects which you represent, but also much the more for your exceeding courtesy in that you have deigned to visit me so unworthy a servant. But good mistress," quod he, "as it were shame for me to confess that ever my heart could yield for fear, so I assure you that my mind cannot be content to induce infirmity by sluggish conceit. But in truth mistress, I am sick," quod he, and therewithal the trembling of his heart had sent up such throbbing into his throat as that his voice—now deprived of breath—commanded the tongue to be still.

When Dame Elynor for compassion distilled into tears and drew towards the window, leaving the other gentlewomen about his bed, who being no less sorry for his grief, yet for that they were none of them so touched in their secret thoughts, they had bolder sprites and freer speech to recomfort him.

Amongst the rest the Lady Frances—who indeed loved him deeply and could best conjecture the cause of his conceits—said unto him:

"Good Trust," quod she, "if any help of physic may cure your malady, I would not have you hurt yourself with these doubts which you seem to retain. If choice of diet may help, behold us here, your cooks, ready to minister all things needful. If company may drive away your annoy, we mean not to leave you solitary. If grief of mind be cause of your infirmity, we all here will offer our devoire to turn it into joy. If mishap have given you cause to fear or dread anything, remember Hope, which never faileth to recomfort an afflicted mind.

And good Trust," quod she, distraining his hand right heartily, "let this simple proof of our poor good wills be so accepted of you, as that it may work thereby the effect of our desires."

F.J. as one in a trance had marked very little of her courteous talk and yet gave her thanks and so held his peace. Whereat the ladies, being all amazed, there became silence in the chamber on all sides. Dame Elynor fearing thereby that she might the more easily be espied, and having now dried up her tears, returned to F.J. recomforting him. By all possible means of common courtesy, promising that since in her sickness he had not only staunched her bleeding, but also by his gentle company and sundry devices of honest pastime had driven away the pensiveness of her mind, she thought herself bound with like willingness to do her best in anything that might restore his health, and taking him by the hand, said further:

"Good servant, if thou bear indeed any true affection to thy poor mistress, start upon thy feet again and let her enjoy thine accustomed service to her comfort. For sure," quod she, "I will never leave to visit this chamber once in a day, until I may have thee down with me."[†]

F.J. hearing the hearty words of his mistress, and perceiving the earnest manner of her pronunciation, began to receive unspeakable comfort in the same and said: "Mistress, your exceeding courtesy were able to revive a man half dead, and to me it is both great comfort and it doth also gald my remembrance with a continual smart of mine own unworthiness. But as I would desire no longer life than till I might be able to deserve some part of your bounty, so I will endeavor myself to live were it but only unto that end, that

---

[†]*have thee down with me.* A bawdy reading is consonant with the preceding verb *enjoy,* 'to take sexual pleasure in', as found in the phrase *enjoy thine accustomed service to her comfort.*

68

I might merit some part of your favor with acceptable service and requite some deal the courtesy of all these other fair ladies, who have so far, above my deserts, deigned to do me good."

Thus said, the ladies tarried not long before they were called to evensong, when his mistress taking his hand, kissed it saying: "Farewell good servant, and I pray thee suffer not the malice of thy sickness to overcome the gentleness of thy good heart."

F.J. ravished with joy suffered them all to depart and was not able to pronounce one word. After their departure, he 'gan cast in his mind the exceeding courtesy used towards him by them all, but above all other the bounty of his mistress, and therewithal took a sound and firm opinion that it was not possible for her to counterfeit so deeply—as indeed I believe that she then did not—whereby he suddenly felt his heart greatly eased and began in himself thus to reason:

"Was ever man[†] of so wretched a heart? I am the most bounden to love," quod he, "of all them that ever[†] professed his service. I enjoy one the fairest that ever was found, and I find her the kindest that ever was heard of. Yet in mine own wicked heart I could villainously conceive that of her, which being compared with the rest of her virtues is not possible to harbor in so noble a mind. Hereby I have brought myself without cause into this feebleness and good reason that for so high an offense I should be punished with great infirmity. What shall I then do: yield to the same? No, but according to my late protestation I will recomfort this languishing mind of mine to the end I may live but only to

---

[†]*ever man*. E. Vere man; more *ver*-words pepper this page.

[†]*ever*. as a margination *ver*-word in the original, with a following hyphenation occurrence in the original text of the same word as **e/ver**; for the significance of margination and its special case hyphenation, see the appendix to the essay following the text.

69

do penance for this so notable a crime so rashly committed."

And thus saying, he start from his bed and 'gan to walk towards the window, but the venomous serpent, which—as before I rehearsed—had stung him, could not be content that these medicines applied by the mouth of his gentle mistress should so soon restore him to guerison.[†] And although indeed they were such Mithridate[†] to F.J. as that they had now expelled the rancor of the poison, yet that ugly hellish monster had left behind her in the most secret of his bosom, even between the mind and the man, one of her familiars named Suspect, which 'gan work in the weak sprites of F.J. effects of no less peril than before he had conceived.

His head swelling with these troublesome toys and his heart swimming in the tempests of tossing fantasy, he felt his legs so feeble that he was constrained to lie down on his bed again, and repeating in his own remembrance every word that his mistress had spoken unto him, he 'gan to dread that she had brought the willow branch to beat him with, in token that he was of her forsaken. For so lovers do most commonly expound the willow garland, and this to think did cut his heart in twain.

A wonderful change and here a little to stay you, I will describe—for I think you have not read it in Ariosto—the beginning, the fall, the return, and the being of this hellish bird, who indeed may well be counted a very limb of the devil. Many years since, one of the most dreadful dastards in the world, and one of them that first devised to wear his beard at length, lest the barber might do him a good turn sooner than he looked for it, and yet not so soon as he

---

[†]*guerison.* health.
[†]*Mithridate.* remedy against poison, as King Mithridates was believed to have built up immunity by daily ingesting trace amounts of poison.

deserved, had builded for his security a pile on the highest and most inaccessible mount of all his territories, the which being fortified with strong walls and environed with deep ditches, had no place of entry but one only door so straight and narrow as might by any possibility receive the body of one living man, from which he ascended up a ladder and so creeping through a marvelous straight hole attained to his lodging, the which was so dark and obscure as scarcely either sun or air could enter into it.

Thus he devised to lodge in safety and for the more surety 'gan trust none other letting down this ladder but only his wife, and at the foot thereof kept always by daylight a fierce mastiff close enkenneled, which never saw nor heard the face or voice of any other creature but only of them two. Him by night he trusted with the scout of this pretty passage, having nevertheless between him and this dog a double door with treble locks, quadruple bars and before all a port coulez[†] of iron. Neither yet could he be so hearty as to sleep until he had caused a guard of servants—whom he kept abroad for that purpose—to search all the corners adjoining to his fortress. And then between fearful sweat and shivering cold, with one eye open and the other closed, he stole sometimes a broken sleep, divided with many terrible dreams.

In this sort the wretch lived all too long, until at last his wife, being not able any longer to support this hellish life, grew so hearty as with his own knife to dispatch his carcass out of this earthly purgatory, the which being done, his soul, and good reason, was quickly conveyed by Carone[†] unto hell. There Rhadamanthus,[†] judge of that bench, commanded him quickly to be thrust into a boiling pool. And

---

†*port coulez.* portcullis, iron gate to a castle that is raised and lowered.
†*Carone.* Charon of Greek mythology, ferrier of dead souls across the River Styx.
†*Rhadamanthus.* a judge in the lower world.

being therein plunged very often, he never shrieked or cried, if called as his other companions there cried, but seemed so lightly to esteem it that the judge thought meet to condemn him unto the most terrible place where are such torments as neither pen can write, tongue express, or thought conceive. But the miser, even there, seemed to smile and to make small account of his punishment.

Rhadamanthus hereof informed sent for him and demanded the cause why he made so light of his durance? He answered that whiles he lived on earth, he was so continually afflicted and oppressed with suspicion as that now—only to think that he was out of those meditations—was sufficient armor to defend him from all other torments. Rhadamanthus, astonied hereat, 'gan call together the senators of that kingdom and propounded this question: how and by what punishment they might devise to touch him according to his deserts? And hereupon fell great disputation, at last being considered that he had already been plunged in the most unspeakable torments and thereat little or nothing had changed countenance, therewithal that no soul was sent unto them to be relieved of his smart, but rather to be punished for his former delights. It was concluded by the general council that he should be eftsoons sent into the world and restored to the same body wherein he first had his resiance,[†] so to remain for perpetuity and never to depart nor to perish. Thus this body and soul being once again united and now eftsoons with the same pestilence infected, he became of a suspicious man Suspicion itself.

And now the wretch remembering the treason of his wife, who had so willingly dispatched him once before, 'gan utterly abhor her and fled her company, searching in all countries some place of better assurance. And when he had in vain trod on the most part of the earth, he embarked

---

[†]*resiance.* residence.

himself to find some unknown island wherein he might frame some new habitation. And finding none so commodious as he desired, he fortuned sailing along by the shore to espy a rock more than six hundred cubits high, which hung so suspiciously over the seas as though it would threaten to fall at every little blast. This did Suspicion imagine to be a fit foundation whereon he might build his second bower.

He forsook his boat and traveled by land to espy what entry or access might be made unto the same and found from land no manner of entry or access, unless it were that some courteous bird of the air would be ambassador or convey some engines, as whilom[†] the eagle did carry Ganymedes[†] into heaven.

He then returned to seas, and approaching near to his rock, found a small stream of fresh water issuing out of the same into the seas, the which, although it were so little and so straight, as might uneathes[†] receive a boat of bigness to carry one living creature at once. Yet in his conceit he thought it more large and spacious[†] than that broad way called of our forefathers *Via Appia*, or than that other named *Flaminia*.[†] He abandoned his bark, and putting off his clothes, adventured, for he was now assured not to drown, to wade and swim against the stream of this unknown brook, the which—a wondrous thing to tell and scarcely to be believed—came down from the very top and height of this rock. And by the way[†] he found six straight and dang-

---

[†]*whilom*. formerly.

[†]*Ganymedes*. Ganymede, Jupiter's page and cupbearer, who according to classical myth was conveyed to heaven by an eagle.

[†]*uneathes*. scarcely.

[†]**large and spacious**. one of many subtle indications that our novelist is Shakespeare; cf. *Wilt thou whose will is **large and spacious**,* as appears in *Sonnet 135.*

[†]*Via Appia ... Flaminia*. major roads of antiquity.

[†]*by the way*. along the way.

erous places where the water seemed to stay his course, passing under six straight and low bridges, and hard by every of those places a pile raised up in manner of a bulwark, the which were hollow in such sort as lodgings and other places necessary might in them commodiously be devised by such one as could endure the hellishness of the place. Passing by these he attained with much pain unto the top of the rock, the which he found hollowed as the rest and far more fit for his security than otherwise apt for any commodity. There 'gan Suspicion determine to nestle himself and having now placed six chosen porters, to wit, Dread, Mistrust, Wrath, Desperation, Frenzy, and Fury, at these six strange bulwarks, he lodged himself in the seventh all alone, for he trusted no company.

But ever mistrusting that his wife should eftsoons find him out, therein he shrieketh continually like to a screech owl to keep the watch waking, never content to sleep by day or by night, but to be sure that he should not oversleep himself, 'gan stuff his couch with porpentine's[†] quills to the end that when heavy sleep overcame him and he thereby should be constrained to charge his pallet with more heavy burden, those plumes might then prick through and so awake him.

His garments were steel upon iron and that iron upon iron and iron again, and the more he was armed, the less he trusted to be out of danger. He chopped and changed continually now this, now that, new keys, new locks, ditches new scoured and walls newly fortified, and thus always uncontented liveth this wretched hellhound Suspicion in this hellish dungeon of habitation, from whence he never removeth his foot, but only in the dead and silent nights, when he may be assured that all creatures but himself are whelmed in sound sleep. And then with stealing steps he

---

[†]*portentine's*. porcupine's.

74

stalketh about the earth, infecting, tormenting, and bearing all kinds of people with some part of his afflictions, but especially such as either do fit in chair of greatest dignity and estimation, or else such as have achieved some dear and rare emprise. Those above all others he continually galdeth with fresh wounds of dread, lest they might lose and forgo the rooms whereunto with such long travail and good haps they had attained. And by this means percase he had crept into the bosom of F.J. who, as is before declared, did erst swim in the deepest seas of earthly delights.

Now then I must think it high time to return unto him, who being now through feebleness eftsoons cast down upon his bed, 'gan cast in his inward meditations all things passed, and as one thoroughly puffed up and filled with one peevish conceit, could think upon nothing else, and yet accusing his own guilty conscience to be infected with jealousy, did compile this translation of Ariosto's thirty-first song as followeth.

What state to man, so sweet and pleasant were,
As to be tied in links of worthy love?
What life so blisst and happy might appear,
As for to serve Cupid that god above?
If that our minds we not sometimes infect,
With dread, with fear, with care, with cold suspect:
With deep despair, with furious frenzy,
Handmaids to her, whom we call jealousy.

For ev'ry other sop of sour chance,
Which lovers taste amid their sweet delight,
Increaseth joy and doth their love advance,
In pleasures place to have more perfect plight.
The thirsty mouth thinks water hath good taste,
The hungry jaws are pleased with each repast:

SECRET SHAKESPEARE'S

Who hath not proved what dearth by wars doth grow,
Cannot of peace the pleasant plenties know.

And though with eye we see not ev'ry joy,
Yet may the mind full well support the same,
An absent life long led in great annoy
When presence comes doth turn from grief to game,
*   To serve without reward is thought great pain,*
*   But if despair do not therewith remain,*
It may be born for right rewards at last,
Follow true service though they come not fast.

Disdains, repulses, finally each ill,
Each smart, each pain, of love each bitter taste,
To think on them 'gan frame the lover's will,
To like each joy, the more that comes at last.
*   But this infernal plague if once it touch,*
*   Or venom once the lover's mind with grutch,*[†]
All feasts and joys that afterwards befall,
The lover counts them light or naught at all.

This is that sore, this is that poisoned wound,
The which to heal, nor salve nor ointments serve,
Nor charm of words nor image can be found,
Nor observance of stars can it preserve,
*   Nor all the art of magic can prevail,*
*   Which Zoroastes found for our avail.*
O cruel plague above all sorrow's smart,
With desperate death thou slay'st the lover's heart.

And me even now, thy gall hath so infect,
As all the joys which ever lover[†] *found,*

[†]*grutch.* grudge, complaint.
[†]*ever lover.* with a double dose of *ver*-play, viz. **ever lover**.

And all good haps, that ever Troilus' sect,
Achievèd yet above the luckless ground
Can never sweeten once my mouth with mell,
Nor bring my thoughts again in rest to dwell.
Of thy mad moods and of naught else I think,
In such like seas, fair Bradamant did sink.
                        F. J.

This is the translation of Ariosto his thirty-first song, all
but the last staff, which seemeth as an allegory applied to
the rest. It will please none but learnèd ears. He was tied to
the invention, troubled in mind, etc., so I leave it to your
judgment and return to F.J., who continued on his bed until
his bountiful mistress with the company of the other courteous dames returned after supper to his chamber, at their
first entry:

"Why how now servant," quod Dame Elynor, "we hoped to have found you on foot?"

"Mistress," quod F.J., "I have assayed my feet since
your departure, but I find them yet unable to support my
heavy body and therefore am constrained as you see to
acquaint myself with these pillows."

"Servant," said she, "I am right sorry thereof, but since
it is of necessity to bear sickness, I will employ my devoir
to allay some part of your pains and to refresh your weary
limbs with some comfortable matter," and therewithal calling her handmaid, delivered unto her a bunch of pretty little
keys, and whispering in her ear, dispatched her towards her
chamber.

The maid tarried not long, but returned with a little casket, the which her mistress took, opened and drew out of
the same much fine linen, amongst the which she took a
pillowbear† very fine and sweet, which although it were of

---

†*pillowbear.* pillowcase.

itself as sweet as might be, being of long time kept in that odoriferous chest, yet did she with damask water[†]—and that the best that might be I warrant you—all to sprinkle it with her own hands, which in my conceit might much a-mend the matter, then calling for a fresh pillow, sent her maid to air the same and at her return put on this thus perfumed pillowbear.

In meantime also she had with her own hands attired her servant's head in a fair wrought kerchief taken out of the same casket, then laid him down upon this fresh and plea-sant place, and prettily as it were in sport, bedewed his temples with sweet water which she had ready in a casting bottle of gold, kissing his cheek and saying:

"Good servant, be whole, for I might not long endure thus to attend thee, and yet the love that I bear towards thee cannot be content to see thee languish."

"Mistress," said F.J., and that with a trembling voice, "assure yourself that if there remain in me any spark of life or possibility of recovery, then may this excellent bounty of yours be sufficient to revive me without any further travail or pain unto your person, for whom I am highly to blame in that I do not spare to put you unto this trouble. And better it were that such a wretch as I had died unknown than that by your exceeding courtesy you should fall into any malady, either by resorting unto me or by these your pains taken about me."

"Servant," quod she, "all pleasures seem painful to them that take no delight therein, and likewise all toil seemeth pleasant to such as set their felicity in the same, but for me be you sure, I do it with so good a will that I can take no hurt thereby, unless I shall perceive that it be rejected or neglected, as unprofitable or uncomfortable unto you."

[†]*damask water*. rosewater.

"To me mistress," quod F.J., "it is such pleasure as neither my feeble tongue can express nor my troubled mind conceive."

"Why, are you troubled in mind then servant?" quod Dame Elynor.

F.J., now blushing, answered: "But even as all sick men be, mistress."

Herewith they stayed their talk awhile, and the first that brake silence was the Lady Frances, who said: "And to drive away the troubles of your mind, good Trust, I would be glad if we could devise some pastime amongst us to keep you company, for I remember that with such devices you did greatly recomfort this fair lady when she languished in like sort."

"She languished indeed, gentle Hope," quod F.J., "but God forbid that she had languished in like sort."

"Everybody thinketh their grief greatest," quod Dame Elynor, "but indeed whether my grief were the more or the less, I am right sorry that yours is such as it is. And to assay whether our passions proceeded of like cause or not, I would we could—according to this lady's saying—devise some like pastimes to try if your malady would be cured with like medicines."

A gentlewoman of the company whom I have not hitherto named, and that for good respects lest her name might altogether disclose the rest,[†] 'gan thus propound: "We have accustomed," quod she, "heretofore in most of our games to choose a king or queen, and he or she during their government have charged every of us either with commandments or questions as best seemed to their majesty. Wherein to speak mine opinion, we have given over large a scope, neither seemeth it reasonable that one should have

---

[†] *her name ... disclose the rest.* Prouty [1942: 254] insightfully considers this phrase "a clue to the fact that the story does concern real people."

the power to discover the thoughts, or at least to bridle the affects of all the rest. And though indeed in questioning, which doth of the twain more nearly touch the mind, everyone is at free liberty to answer what they list. Yet oft have I heard a question demanded in such sort, and upon such sudden, that it hath been hardly answered without moaning matter of contention. And in commands also, sometimes it happeneth one to be commanded unto such service, as either they are unfit to accomplish, and then the party's weakness is thereby detected, or else to do something that they would not, whereof ensueth more grutch[†] than game. Wherefore in mine opinion, we shall do well to choose by lot amongst us a governor, who for that it shall be sufficient preeminence to use the charge of majesty, shall be bound to give sentence upon all such arguments and questions as we shall orderly propound unto them, and from him or her, as from an oracle, we will receive answer and deciding of our litigious causes."

This dame had stuff in her, an old courtier, and a wily wench, whom for this discourse I will name Pergo, lest her name natural were too broad before,[†] and might not drink of all waters.[†] Well this proportion of Pergo pleased them well, and by lot it happened that F.J. must be moderator of these matters and collector of these causes, the which being so constituted, the Lady Elynor said unto this Dame Pergo: "You have devised this pastime," quod she, "and because

---

[†]*grutch*. grudge.

[†]*too broad before*. too well-known; admitted in Prouty [1942: 254] as evidence that real-life Elizabethans are depicted, as also the author's admission in the revision that some readers had construed the novel as "scandalous", cf. Cunliffe [1907, Vol. I: 3] or Hazlitt [1869].

[†]*drink of all waters*. might not be considered discrete to all; the phrase *all waters* was used to signify a universal quantifier, as also in *Twelfth Night: Nay I am for all waters*. Pigman [2000: 588] notes, but does not explain, the existence of the related phrase, which is that our novelist was Oxford, who later wrote under the *Shakespeare* pseudonym.

we think you to be most expert in the handling thereof, do you propound the first question and we shall be both the more ready and able to follow your example."

The Lady Pergo refused not, but began on this wise. "Noble governor," quod she, "amongst the adventures that have befallen me, I remember especially this one, that in youth it was my chance to be beloved of a very courtlike young gentleman, who abode near the place wherein my parents had their resiance. This gentleman, whether it were for beauty or for any other respect that he saw in me, I know not, but he was enamored of me and that with an exceeding vehement passion and of such force were his affects that notwithstanding many repulses which he had received at my hands, he seemed daily to grow in the renewing of his desires. I on the other side, although I could by no means mislike of him by any good reason, considering that he was of birth no way inferior unto me, of possessions not to be disdained, of person right comely, of behavior courtly, of manners modest, of mind liberal, and of virtuous disposition. Yet such was the gaiety of my mind as that I could not be content to lend him overlarge thongs of my love, but always dangerously behaved myself towards him, and in such sort as he could neither take comfort of mine answers, nor yet once find himself requited with one good look for all his travail. This notwithstanding, the worthy knight continued his suit with no less vehement affection than erst he had begun it, even by the space of seven years.

"At the last, whether discomfited by my dealings or tired by long travail, or that he had percase lit upon the lake that is in the forest of Ardena[†] and so in haste and all thirsty had drunk some drops of disdain whereby his hot flames

---

[†]*forest of Ardena.* Forest of Ardennes of *Orlando Furioso* is the presumed source, in the midst of which is situated a Fountain of Hate.

were quenched, or that he had undertaken to serve no longer but his just term of apprenticehood, or that the teeth of time had gnawn and tired his dullèd sprites in such sort as that all benumbed he was constrained to use some other artificial[†] balm for the quickening of his senses, or by what cause moved I know not, he did not only leave his long continued suit, but—as I have since perceived—grew to hate me more deadly than before I had disdained him.

"At the first beginning of his retire I perceived not his hatred, but imagined that being overwearied, he had withdrawn himself for a time. And considering his worthiness, therewithal his constancy of long time proved, I thought that I could not in the whole world find out a fitter match to bestow myself than on so worthy a person, wherefore I did by all possible means procure that he might eftsoons use his accustomed repair unto my parents. And further, in all places where I happened to meet him, I used all the courtesies towards him that might be contained within the bonds of modesty, but all was in vain, for he was now become more dangerous to be won than the haggard falcon.[†]

"Our lots being thus unluckily changed, I grew to burn in desire and the more dangerous that he showed himself unto me, the more earnest I was by all means to procure his

---

[†]*artificial.* skillfully produced.
[†]*haggard falcon.* falcon or hawk captured as an adult and therefore likely to be wild and unmanageable; its metaphoric extension to womankind is typical of Shakespeare; cf. *Shakespeare's Fingerprints*, Chapter 9, where additional examples are adduced, including the following comparison due to J. Thomas Looney.

DE VERE: *The stricken deer hath help to heal his wound,*
           *The **haggard** hawk with toil is made full tame,*
           The strongest tower the canon lays on ground,
           The wisest wit that ever had the fame,

SHAKESPEARE: *Like the **haggard**, check at every feather*
               That comes before his eye

consent of love. At the last I might perceive that not only he disdained me, but as me thought,[†] boiled in hatred against me. And the time that I thus continued tormented with these thoughts was also just the space of seven years. Finally when I perceived no remedy for my perplexities, I assayed by absence to wear away this malady and therefore utterly refused to come in his presence, yea or almost in any other company, whereby I have consumed in lost time the flower of my youth and am become as you see—what with years and what with the tormenting passions of love— pale, wan, and full of wrinkles. Nevertheless, I have thereby gained thus much, that at last I have wound myself clear out of Cupid's chains and remain careless at liberty.

"Now mark to what end I tell you this. First seven years passed, in the which I could never be content to yield unto his just desires. Next other seven years I spent in seeking to recover his lost love. And sithens both those seven years there are, even now on Saint Valentine's Day last, other seven years passed in the which neither I have desired to see him nor he hath coveted to hear of me.

"My parents now perceiving how the crow's foot is crept under mine eye, and remembering the long suit that this gentleman had in youth spent on me, considering therewithal that green youth is well mellowed in us both, have of late sought to persuade a marriage between us, the which the knight hath not refused to hear of, and I have not disdained to think on. By their mediation we have been eftsoons brought to parley, wherein over and besides the ripping up of many old griefs, this hath been chiefly rehearsed and objected between us, what wrong and injury each of us hath done to other, and hereabouts we have fallen to sharp contention. He alleged that much greater is the wrong which I have done unto him than that repulse which he hath

---

[†]*me thought.* past tense of *methinks.*

sithens used to me, and I have affirmed the contrary; the matter yet hangeth in variance.

"Now, of you worthy governor I would be most glad to hear this question decided, remembering that there was no difference in the times between us. And surely, unless your judgment help me, I am afraid my marriage will be marred and I may go lead apes in hell."[†]

F.J. answered: "Good Pergo, I am sorry to hear so lamentable a discourse of your luckless love and much the sorrier in that I must needs give sentence against you. For surely great was the wrong that either of you have done to other and greater was the needless grief which causeless each of you hath conceived in this long time, but greatest in my judgment hath been both the wrong and the grief of the knight in that notwithstanding his deserts—which yourself confess—he never enjoyed any guerdon[†] of love at your hands. And you, as you allege, did enjoy his love of long time together, so that by the reckoning it will fall out—al-

---

[†]*lead apes in hell*. Many Shakespearean critics have read the phrase as a posthumous retribution for failure to marry and bear children in the context of *The Taming of the Shrew* and *Much Ado About Nothing;* in the latter Beatrice remarks: *Therefore I will ... lead his apes into hell*, a quip followed by an ingenious twist. Kuhl [1925] claims that the phrase originated in the context of punishment for adultery. Summary discussion of analogous phrases, some missed by Kuhl, is provided in *Never and For Ever,* including the following associated with Oxford's *Weever* pseudonym, one of several pseudonyms that we term a *veronym*.

A cloister woman mewed up in a cell,
To die a maid and then lead apes in hell.

[†]*guerdon*. reward, gift. Ellis [1973: 137] notes that *guerdon* could be pronounced as *garden* with a pun on the female body, as attested in *Love's Labour's Lost* where *guerdon* and *gardon* are brought together for punning wordplay. Within the present context, construal of *enjoy* as 'take sexual pleasure in' would support the claim to a bawdy interpretation, another parallel with Shakespeare that cries out for explanation and finds the same in the identification of Shakespeare with our author.

though being blinded in your own conceit you see it not—
that of the onc and twenty years you enjoyed his love seven
at the least, but that ever he enjoyed yours we cannot perceive. And much greater is the wrong that rewardeth evil
for good than that which requireth tip for tap.

Further, it seemed that where you went about in time to
try him, you did altogether lose time which can never be recovered and not only left your own time whereof you
would seem now to lament, but also compelled him to lease
his time, which he might—be it spoken without offense to
you—have bestowed in some other worthy place. And
therefore, as that grief is much greater which hath no kind
of comfort to allay it, so much more is that wrong which
altogether without cause is offered."

"And I," said Pergo, "must needs think that much easier
is it for them to endure grief which never tasted of joy, and
much less is that wrong which is so willingly proffered to
be by recompense restored. For it, this knight will confess
that he never had cause to rejoice in all the time of his service, then with better contentation might he abide grief than
I, who having tasted of the delight which I did secretly conceive of his deserts, do think each grief a present death by
the remembrance of those forepassèd thoughts. And less
wrong seemeth it to be destitute of the thing which was never obtained than to be deprived of a jewel whereof we
have been already possessed. So that under your correction
I might conclude that greater hath been my grief and injury
sustained than that of the knight."

To whom F.J. replied: "As touching delight, it may not
be denied but that every lover doth take delight in the inward contemplation of his mind to think of the worthiness
of his beloved, and therefore you may not allege that the
knight had never cause to rejoice, unless you will altogether
condemn yourself of unworthiness. Marry, if you will say
that he tasted not the delights that lovers seek, then mark

who was the cause but yourself? And if you would accuse him of like ingratitude, for that he disdained you in the latter seven years, whenas he might by accepting your love have recompensed himself of all former wrongs, you must remember therewithal that the cruelty by you showed towards him was such that he could by no means perceive that your change proceeded of good will, but rather eftsoons to hold him enchained in unknown links of subtle dealings. And therefore not without cause he doubted you.

"And yet without cause you rejected him. He had often sought Occasion, but by your refusals he could never find him.[†] You, having Occasion fast by the foretop,[†] did dally with him so long, till at last he slipped his head from you, and then catching at the bald noodle,[†] you found yourself the cause and yet you would accuse another. To conclude, greater is the grief that is sustained without desert and much more is the wrong that is offered without cause."

Thus F.J. decided the question propounded by Pergo and expected that some other dame should propound another. But his mistress, having her hand on another halfpenny, 'gan thus say unto him: "Servant, this pastime is good and such as I must needs like of to drive away your pensive thoughts. But sleeping time approacheth and I fear we disquiet you, wherefore the rest of this time we will, if so like you, bestow in trimming up your bed. And tomorrow we shall meet here and renew this new begun game with Madam Pergo."

[†]*find him.* i.e. Occasion, opportunity personified.

[†]*foretop.* hair of Occasion, the latter personified.

[†]*bald noodle.* Opportunity must be seized when it presents itself, the metaphor of the hair, or otherwise it will be lost, the metaphor of the bald noodle, the hairless region towards the back of the head. Thus, Occasion was depicted as a woman standing on the wheel of fortune with her hair blowing to the fore, while here the conceit is naturally masculine by identification with Pergo's beloved knight.

"Mistress," quod F.J., "I must obey your will and most humbly thank you of your great goodness and all these ladies for their courtesy. Even so, requiring you that you will no further trouble yourselves about me, but let my servant alone with conducting me to bed."

"Yes servant," quod she, "I will see if you can sleep any better in my sheets," and therewith commanded her handmaid to fetch a pair of clean sheets, the which being brought, marvelous fine and sweet, the ladies Frances and Elynor did courteously unfold them and laid them on the bed, which done they also entreated F.J. to unclothe him and go to bed.

Being laid, his mistress dressed and couched the clothes about him, sithens moistened his temples with rosewater, gave him handkerchiefs and other fresh linen about him, in doing whereof, she whispered in his ear, saying: "Servant, this night I will be with thee," and after with the rest of the dames gave him goodnight and departed, leaving F.J. in a trance between hope and despair, trust and mistrust.

Thus he lay ravished, commanding his servant to go to bed and feigning that himself would assay if he could sleep. About ten or eleven of the clock came his mistress in her nightgown, who knowing all privy ways in that house very perfectly, had conveyed herself into F.J.'s chamber, unseen and unperceived, and being now come unto his bedside kneeled down and laying her arm over him said these or like words:

"My good servant, if thou knewest what perplexities I suffer in beholding of thine infirmities, it might then suffice either utterly to drive away thy malady or much more to augment thy griefs. For I know thou lovest me and I think also that thou hast had sufficient proof of mine unfeignèd good will, in remembrance whereof I fall into sundry passions. First, I count the happy lots of our first acquaintance and therein I call to mind the equality of our affections, for I think that there were never two lovers con-joined with freer consent on both parties. And if my over-hasty delivery[†] of yielding words be not wrested hereafter to my condemnation, I can then assure myself to escape forever without desert of any reproof. Here withal I cannot forget the sundry adventures happened since we became one heart divided in two[†] bodies, all which have been both happily achieved and delectably enjoyed. What resteth then to consider but this thy present state: the first corrosive that I have felt and the last cordial that I look for, the end of my joys and the beginning of my torments?"

And hereat her salt tears 'gan bathe the dying lips of her servant, who hearing these words and well considering her demeanor, began now to accuse himself of such and so heinous treason as that his guilty heart was constrained to yield unto a just scourge for the same. He swooned under her arm, the which when she perceived, it were hard to tell what fears did most affright her.

But I have heard my friend F.J. confess that he was in a happy trance and thought himself for divers causes unhap-pily revived. For surely I have heard him affirm that to die in such a passion had been rather pleasant than like to pangs of death. It were hard now to rehearse how he was revived, since there were none present but he dying who could not declare, and she living who would not disclose, so much as I mean to bewray, for my friend F.J. hath to me imported that, returning to life, the first thing which he felt was that his good mistress lay pressing his breast with the

---

[†]*overhasty delivery.* with margination *ver*-play via a catchword in the original; margination wordplay is illustrated in the following essay.

[†]*one heart **divided** in **two**.* The triad of *one, divided,* and *two* is typically Shakespearean, as in the opening quatrain of *Sonnet 36:*

*Let me confess that we **two** must be twain,*
*Although our un**divided** loves are **one**.*

whole weight of her body and biting his lips with her friendly teeth.

And peradventure she refrained, either of courtesy towards him or for womanish fear, to hurt her tender hand to strike him on the cheeks in such sort as they do that strive to call again a dying creature and therefore thought this the aptest mean to reduce him unto remembrance.

F.J. now awaked could no less do than of his courteous nature, received his mistress into his bed, who, as one that knew that way better than how to help his swooning, 'gan gently strip off her clothes, and lovingly embracing him, 'gan demand of him in this sort:

"Alas good servant," quod she, "what kind of malady is this that so extremely doth torment thee?"

F.J. with fainting speech answered: "Mistress, as for my malady, it hath been easily cured by your bountiful medicines applied. But I must confess that in receiving that guerison at your hands, I have been constrained to fall into an ecstasy, through the galding remembrance of mine own unworthiness. Nevertheless, good mistress, since I perceive such fidelity remaining between us, as that few words will persuade such trust as lovers ought to embrace, let these few words suffice to crave your pardon and do eftsoons power upon me—your unworthy servant—the abundant waves of your accustomed clemency. For I must confess that I have so highly offended you, as—but your goodness surpass the malice of my conceits—I must remain, and that right worthily, to the severe punishment of my deserts. And so should you but lose him who hath cast away himself and neither can accuse you, nor dare excuse himself of the crime."

Dame Elynor, who had rather have found her servant perfectly revived than thus with strange conceits encumbered, and musing much at his dark speech, became importunate to know with certainty of his thoughts. And F.J. as one not master of himself 'gan at the last plainly confess how he had mistrusted the change of her vowèd affections. Yea, and that more was, he plainly expressed with whom, of whom, by whom, and to whom she bent her better liking.

Now, here I would demand of you and such other as are expert: is there any greater impediment to the fruition of a lover's delights than to be mistrusted? Or rather, is it not the ready way to 'rase[†] all love and former good will out of remembrance to tell a guilty mind that you do mistrust it? It should seem yes by Dame Elynor, who began now to take the matter hotly, and of such vehemency were her fancies that she now fell into flat defiance with F.J., who although he sought by many fair words to temper her choleric passions and by yielding herself to yet the conquest of another, yet could he by no means determine the quarrel.

The soft pillows, being present at all these hot words, put forth themselves as mediators for a truce between these enemies and desired that—if they would needs fight—it might be in their presence but only one push of the pike[†] and so from thenceforth to become friends again for ever. But the dame denied flatly, alleging that she found no cause at all to use such courtesy unto such a recreant, adding further many words of great reproach, the which did so enrage F.J. as that having now forgotten all former courtesies, he drew upon his new professed enemy and bare her up with such a violence against the bolster that before she could prepare the ward,[†] he thrust her through both hands &c.[†]

[†] *'rase.* erase.

[†] *pike.* a long spear and here a play on the male organ, hence *push.*

[†] *prepare the ward.* expression from fencing for the assumption of a defensive position.

[†] *&c.* To be read 'and caetera', with an allusion to the *caetera* or the other, i.e. the female pudendum, as witnessed clearly in lines from one of the author's poems found in *The Phoenix Nest,* provided at the foot of the following page:

whereby the dame swooning for fear was constrained, for a time, to abandon her body to the enemy's courtesy.

At last when she came to herself, she rose suddenly and determined to save herself by flight, leaving F.J. with many despiteful words and swearing that he should never, eftsoons, take her at the like advantage, the which oath she kept better than her former professed good will. And having now recovered her chamber—because she found her hurt to be nothing dangerous—I doubt not but she slept quietly the rest of the night, as F.J., also persuading himself that he should with convenient leisure recover her from this hagger[†] conceit, took some better rest towards the morning than he had done in many nights forepassed.

So let them both sleep whiles I turn my pen unto the before-named secretary, who being, as I said, come lately from London, had made many proffers to renew his accustomed consultations. But the sorrow which his mistress had conceived in F.J. his sickness,[†] together with her continual repair to him during the same, had been such lets unto his attempts, as it was long time before he could obtain audience. At the last these new accidents fell so favorably for the furtherance of his cause that he came to his mistress' presence and there pleaded for himself.

Now, if I should at large write his allegations, together with her subtle answers, I should but cumber your ears with unpleasant rehearsal of feminine frailty.[†] To be short, the late disdainful mood which she had conceived against F.J.,

---

To wish, to dally, and to offer game,
*To coy, to court, & **caetera to do**.*
*Forgive me chastness, if in **terms of shame**,*
To thy renown, I paint what longs thereto.

[†]*hagger*. haggard, clarified in an earlier note.
[†]*F.J. his sickness*. F.J.'s sickness.
[†]*feminine frailty*. reminiscent of Hamlet's *frailty, thy name is woman*.

together with a scruple which lay in her conscience touching the eleventh article of her belief,[†] moved her presently with better will to consult with this secretary, as well upon a speedy revenge of her late received wrongs, as also upon the reformation of her religion.

And in very deed it fell out that the secretary, having been of long time absent and thereby his quills and pēnes[†] not worn so near as they were wont to be, did now prick such fair large notes[†] that his mistress liked better to sing faburden[†] under him than to descant[†] any longer upon F.J.'s plainsong.[†]

And thus they continued in good accord, until it fortuned that Dame Frances came into her chamber upon such sudden as she had like to have marred all the music. Well, they conveyed their clefs as closely as they could,[†] but yet

---

[†]*eleventh article of her belief.* the eleventh article of *The Thirty-Nine Articles* of the Church of England, emphasizing faith at the expense of works or deservings; Lawlis [1967: 92] claims that Elinor's belief and religion are thereby reduced to the physical and worldly.

[†]*pēnes.* original spelling retained to preserve the play on the secretary's penis; cf. the essay following the novel.

[†]*prick ... notes.* with wordplay on the male and female genitalia via *prick* and *notes*, the latter via the commoner *nought.*

[†]*faburden.* undersong, with a quibble on the supine coital position.

[†]*descant.* melody sung above a musical theme, hence the superior coital position, with possible genital play via *des-cant;* cf. essay following; it is especially revealing that similar bawdy play is utilized in *The Rape of Lucrece,* where *burden* is a variant of *faburden* in the previous note, this similarity providing strong evidence that the name *William Shakespeare* is another pseudonym for our novelist:

> For **burden**-wise I'll hum on Tarquin still,
> While thou on Tereus **descants** better skill.

[†]*plainsong.* monotonous song (without meter), as in Gregorian chant, but here intended as a play on the monotone made upon orgasm, with *sing* intended to relate to coitus, as also *descant.*

[†]*conveyed their clefs as closely as they could.* concealed their base clef and treble clef, i.e. their respective members, as best they could.

not altogether without some suspicion given to the said Dame Frances, who although she could have been content to take any pain in F.J.'s behalf, yet otherwise she would never have bestowed the watching about so worthless a prize.

After womanly salutations they fell into sundry discourses, the secretary still abiding in the chamber with them. At last two or three other gentlewomen of the castle came into Madam Elynor's chamber, who after their *bon jour* did all—*una voce*†—seem to lament the sickness of F.J. and called upon the Dames Elynor and Frances to go visit him again. The Lady Frances courteously consented, but Madam Elinor first alleged that she herself was also sickly, the which she attributed to her late pains taken about F.J. and said that only for that cause she was constrained to keep her bed longer than her accustomed hour.

The dames, but especially the Lady Frances, 'gan straightways conjecture some great cause of sudden change, and so leaving Dame Elynor, walked altogether into the park to take the air of the morning. And as they thus walked it chanced that Dame Pergo heard a cuckoo† chant, who, because the pride of the spring† was now past, cried *cuck cuck cuckoo* in her stammering voice.

---

†*una voce*. in one voice.
†*cuckoo*. bird that lays her eggs into another's nest, hence a reference to cuckoldry.
†*spring*. a subtle reference to the author via *Ver* for 'spring'; utilized for example by de Vere in the following verse from *Flowers*, but also elsewhere, as elaborated in *Never and For Ever:*

> The lusty **Ver** which whilom might exchange
> My grief to joy and then my joy's increase,
> **Springs** now elsewhere and shows to me but strange,
> My winter's woe therefore can never cease:

And later in the same poem, disclosing the author's nobility, illustrated at the foot of the following page:

"Aha," quod Pergo, "this foul bird begins to fly the country[†] and yet before her departure, see how spitefully she can devise to salute us."

"Not us," quod Dame Frances, "but some other whom she hath espied."

Wherewith Dame Pergo looking round about her and espying none other company said: "Why here is nobody but we few women," quod she.

"Thanks be to God the house is not far from us,"[†] quod Dame Frances.

Hereat the wily Pergo, partly perceiving Dame Frances' meaning, replied on this sort: "I understand you not," quod she, "but to leap out of this matter, shall we go visit Master F.J. and see how he doth this morning?"

"Why," quod Dame Frances, "do you suppose that the cuckoo called unto him?"[†]

"Nay marry," quod Pergo, "for, as far as I know, he is not married."

"As who should say," quod Dame Frances, "that the cuckoo envieth none but married folks?"

"I take it so," said Pergo.

The Lady Frances answered: "Yes, sure I have noted as evil luck in love, after the cuckoo's call, to have happened unto divers unmarried folks, as ever I did unto the married. But I can be well content that we go unto Master J, for I promised on the behalf of us all that we would use our best

---

Now ladies you that know by whom I sing,
And feel the winter of such frozen wills:
*Of courtesy yet cause this **noble spring**,*
To send his sun above the highest hills:

[†]*fly the country.* hinting at F.J.'s cessation of playing the role of a cuckold, with an obvious pun on *country*.
[†]*the house is not far from us.* indicating the cuckold is therein and not among the walking party of women.
[†]*that the cuckoo calleth unto him?* that he is the cuckold?

devoire to recomfort him until he had recovered health, and I do much marvel that the Lady Elinor is now become so unwilling to take any travail in his behalf, especially remembering that but yesternight she was so diligent to bring him to bed. But I perceive that all earthly things are subject unto change."[†]

"Even so they be," quod Pergo, "for you may behold the trees which but even this other day were clad in gladsome green,[†] and now their leaves begin to fade and change color."

Thus they passed, talking and walking until they returned unto the castle, whereas they went straight unto F.J.'s chamber and found him in bed.

"Why how now Trust," quod Dame Frances. "Will it be no better?"

"Yes, shortly I hope," quod F.J.

The ladies all saluted him and he gave them the gramercy. At the last Pergo popped this question unto him: "And how have you slept in your mistress' sheets, Master F.J.?" quod she.

"Reasonably well," quod F.J., "but I pray you, where is my mistress this morning?"

"Marry," said Pergo, "we left her in bed scarce well at ease."

"I am the more sore," quod F.J.

"Why Trust," said Mistress Frances, "be of good comfort and assure yourself that here are others who would be as glad of your well doing as your mistress in any respect."

[†]*all earthly things are subject unto change.* typical of the author's concern with Time's devouring nature under other pseudonyms.

[†]*green.* The reason for Pergo's comment may relate to this color word as pun in relation to its Romance root *ver(d)* manifested in the English borrowing *verdant,* for example, and hence to the author's name.

"I ought not to doubt thereof," quod F.J., "having the proof that I have had of your great courtesies, but I thought it my duty to ask for my mistress' being absent."

Thus they passed some time with him until they were called away unto prayers, and that being finished, they went to dinner where they met Dame Elynor attired in a night kerchief after the soolenest[†]—the solemnest fashion I should have said—who looked very drowsily upon all folks unless it were her secretary unto whom she deigned sometime to lend a sweetly glance.

The Lord of the castle demanded of her how F.J. did this morning. She answered that she knew not, for she had not seen him that day.

"You may do well then, daughter," quod the lord, "to go now unto him and to assay if he will eat anything and if here be no meats that like him,[†] I pray you command for him anything that is in my house."

"You must pardon me sir," quod she, "I am sickly disposed and would be loath to take the air."

"Why then go you Mistress Frances," quod he, "and take somebody with you. And I charge you see that he lack nothing."

Mistress Frances was glad of the ambassade and arising from the table with one other gentlewoman took with her a dish of chickens boiled in white broth, saying to her father: "I think this meat meetest for Master J. of any that is here."[†]

"It is so," quod he, "daughter, and if he like not that, cause somewhat else to be dressed for him according to his appetite."

[†]*soolenest.* early instance of a Freudian slip; perhaps 'scantiest' is the intended reading via 'so leanest', consistent with spelling of *so* as *soo*.
[†]*that like him.* that are agreeable with him.
[†]*of any that is here.* i.e. more agreeable than Elinor.

Thus she departed and came to F.J., who being plunged in sundry woes and thrilled with restless thoughts, was now beginning to arise, but seeing the dames, couched down again and said unto them: "Alas fair ladies, you put yourselves to more pains than either I do desire or can deserve."

"Good Trust," quod Dame Frances, "our pains are no greater than duty requireth, nor yet so great as we could vouchsafe in your behalf, and presently my father hath sent us unto you," quod she, "with this pittance. And if your appetite desire any one thing more than other, we are to desire likewise that you will not refrain to call for it."

"Oh my good Hope," quod he. "I perceive that I shall not die as long as you may make me live."

And being now some deal recomforted with the remembrance of his mistress' words which she had used overnight at her first coming, and also thinking that although she parted in choler, it was but justly provoked by himself and that at leisure he should sense some salve for that sore also, he determined to take the comfort of his assurèd Hope and so expel all venoms of mistrust before received. Wherefore raising himself in his bed, he cast a nightgown about his shoulders saying: "It shall never be said that my fainting heart can reject the comfortable cordials of so friendly physicians."

"Now by my troth well said, gentle Trust," quod Dame Frances, "and in so doing assure yourself of guerison with speed."

This thus said, the courteous dame became his carver and he with a bold spirit 'gan taste of her cookery. But the late conflicts of his conceits had so disaquainted his stomach from repasts that he could not well away with meat, and yet, nevertheless, by little and little received some nurture. When his Hope had crammed him as long as she could make him feed, they delivered the rest to the other gentlewoman, who having not dined, fell to her provender in which meanwhile the Lady Frances had much comfortable speech with F.J. and declared that she perceived very well the cause of his malady.

"But my Trust," quod she, "be all whole and remember what I foretold you in the beginning. Nevertheless you must think that there are remedies for all mischiefs, and if you will be ruled by mine advice, we will soon find the mean to ease you of this mishap."

F.J. took comfort in her discretion and friendly kissing her hand, gave her a cartload of thanks for her great good will, promising to put to his uttermost force and evermore[†] to be ruled by her advice. Thus they passed the dinner while the Lady Frances always refusing to declare her conceit of the late change which she perceived in his mistress, for she thought best first to win his will unto conformity by little and little and then in the end to persuade him with necessity. When the other gentlewoman had vittled her, they departed, requiring F.J. to arise and boldly to resist the faintness of his fever, the which he promised and so bad them *a Dio*.[†]

The ladies at their return found the court[†] in Dame Elinor's chamber, who had there assembled her secretary, Dame Pergo, and the rest. There they passed an hour or twain in sundry discourses, wherein Dame Pergo did always cast out some bone for Mistress Frances to gnaw upon, for that indeed she perceived her hearty affection towards F.J., whereat Mistress Frances changed no countenance, but reserved her revenge until a better opportunity.

At last quod Dame Frances unto Mistress Elinor: "And when will you go unto your servant, fair lady?"

"When he is sick and I am whole," quod Dame Elynor.

[†]*evermore*. another pun on the author, as earlier on pages 18 and 22.
[†]*a Dio*. goodbye.
[†]*the court*. suggestive of Elinor's identity, for discussion of which see the authorship essay following.

"That is even now," quod the other, "for how sick he is yourself can witness and how well you are we must bear record."

"You may as well be deceived in my disposition," quod Dame Elynor, "as I was overseen in his sudden alteration, and if he be sick you are meetest to be his physician. For you saw yesterday that my pains did little profit towards his recomfort."

"Yes, surely," said the other, "not only I but all the rest had occasion to judge that your courtesy was his chief comfort."

"Well," quod Dame Elinor, "you know not what I know."

"Nor you what I think," quod Dame Frances.

"Think what you list," quod Elynor.

"Indeed," quod Frances. "I may not think that you care; neither will I die for your displeasure."

And so half angry, she departed. At supper they met again, and the master of the house demanded of his daughter Frances how F.J. did.

"Sir," quod she, "he did eat somewhat at dinner, and sithens I saw him not."

"The more to blame," quod he, "and now I would have all you gentlewomen take of the best meats and go sup with him. For company driveth away carefulness and leave you me here with your leavings alone."

"Nay, sir," quod Mistress Elynor. "I pray you give me leave to bear you company, for I dare not adventure thither."

The Lord of the castle was contented and dispatched away the rest, who taking with them such viands as they thought meetest, went unto F.J.'s chamber, finding him up and walking about to recover strength. Whereat Dame Frances rejoiced and declared how her father had sent that company to attend him at supper. F.J. gave great thanks and

missing now nothing but his mistress thought not good yet
to ask for her, but because he partly guessed the cause of
her absence, he contented himself, hoping that when his
lure was new garnished, he should easily reclaim her from
those coy conceits.

They passed over their supper all in quiet, and soon after
Mistress Frances, being desirous to requite Dame Pergo's
quips, requested that they might continue the pastime
which Dame Pergo had begun over[†] night, whereupon they
all consented and the lot fell unto Dame Frances to propound the second question, who addressing her speech unto
F.J. said in this wise:

"Noble governor, I will rehearse unto you a strange history, not feigned, neither borrowed out of any old authority, but a thing done indeed of late days and not far distant
from this place where we now remain. It chanced that a
gentleman our neighbor, being married to a very fair gentlewoman, lived with her by the space of four or five years
in great contentation, trusting her no less than he loved her,
and yet loving her as much as any man could love a woman. On that other side the gentlewoman had won unto her
beauty[†] a singular commendation for her chaste and modest
behavior. Yet it happened in time that a lusty young gentleman who very often resorted to them obtained that at her
hands which never any man could before him attain. And to
be plain, he won so much in her affections that forgetting
both her own duty and her husband's kindness, she yielded
her body at the commandment of this lover, in which pastime they passed long time by their politic government.[†]

"At last the friends of this lady, and especially three
sisters which she had, espied overmuch familiarity between

[†]*over.* hyphenated in the original, suggesting wordplay on the **O**xford
Vere, viz. *o/ver;* cf. discussion in Appendix to the authorship essay.
[†]*unto her beauty.* in addition to her beauty.
[†]*government.* behavior.

the two lovers. And dreading lest it might break out to their common reproach, took their sister apart and declared that the world did judge scarce well of the repair of that gentleman unto her house and that if she did not foresee it in time, she should not only lose the good credit which she herself had hitherto possessed, but furthermore should disdain their whole race with common obloquy[†] and reproach.

"These and sundry other goodly admonitions of these sisters could not sink in the mind of this gentlewoman, for she did not only stand in defiance what any man could think of her, but also seemed to accuse them that because they saw her estimation, being their younger, to grow above their own, they had therefore devised this mean to set variance between her husband and her.

"The sisters seeing their wholesome counsel so rejected, and her continue still in her obstinate opinion, addressed their speech unto her husband, declaring that the world judged not the best, neither they themselves did very well like of the familiarity between their sister and that gentleman, and therefore advised him to forecast all perils and in time to forbid him his house. The husband, on that other side, had also conceived such a good opinion of his guest and had grown into such a strict familiarity with him that you might with more ease have removed a stone wall than once to make him think amiss, either of his wife or of her lover.

"Yea and immediately after this conference, he would not stick thus to say unto his wife: 'Besse'—for so indeed was her name—'thou hast three such busy-brained sisters as I think shortly their heads will break. They would have me to be jealous of thee.' 'No, no, Besse,' &c. So that he was not only far from any such belief, but furthermore did every day increase his courtesies towards the lover. The

---

[†]*obloquy.* abusive language.

sisters being thus on all sides rejected, and yet perceiving more and more an unseemly behavior between their sister and her minion, began to melt in their own grief. And such was their enraged pretense of revenge that they suborned[†] divers servants in the house to watch so diligently as that this treason might be discovered.

"Amongst the rest, one maid of subtle spirit had so long watched them that at last she espied them go into a chamber together and lock the door to them. Whereupon she ran with all haste possible to her master and told him that if he would come with her, she would show him a very strange sight. The gentleman, suspecting nothing, went with her until he came into a chamber near unto that wherein they had shut themselves, and she pointing her master to the keyhole, bad him look through, where he saw the thing which most might mislike him to behold. Whereat he suddenly drew his dagger and turned towards the maid, who fled from him for fear of mischief. But when he could not overtake her in the heat of his choler, he commanded that she should forthwith truss up that little which she had and to depart his service. And before her departure he found means to talk with her, threatening that if ever she spake any word of this mystery in any place where she should come, it should cost her life.

"The maid for fear departed in silence and the master never changed countenance either to his wife or to her paramour, but feigned unto his wife that he had turned away the maid upon that sudden, for that she had thrown a kitchen knife at him, whiles he went about to correct a fault in her &c.

"Thus the good gentleman drank up his own sweat unseen every day, increasing courtesy to the lover and never changing countenance to his wife in anything, but only that

---

[†]*suborned.* induced to wrongful or unlawful action.

he refrained to have such knowledge of her carnally as he in times past had, and other men have of their wives. In this sort he continued by the space almost of half a year, nevertheless lamenting his mishap in solitary places.

"At last—what moved him I know not—he fell again to company with his wife as other men do, and as I have heard it said he used this policy. Every time that he had knowledge of her, he would leave either in the bed, or in her cushion cloth, or by her looking glass, or in some place where she must needs find it, a piece of money which then was fallen to three halfpence. And I remember they called them 'slips'.[†] Thus he dealt with her continually[†] by the space of four or five months, using her nevertheless very kindly in all other respects and providing for her all things necessary at the first call. But unto his guest he still augmented his courtesy in such sort that you would have thought them to be sworn brothers.

"All this notwithstanding, his wife much musing at these three halfpenny pieces which she found in this sort, and furthermore, having sundry times found her husband in solitary places making great lamentation, she grew inquisitive what should be the secret cause of these alterations, unto whom he would none otherwise answer, but that any man should find occasion to be more pensive at one time than at another.

"The wife notwithstanding, increasing her suspect, imported the same unto her lover, alleging therewithal that she doubted very much lest her husband had some vehement suspicion of their affairs. The lover encouraged her and likewise declared that if she would be importunate to enquire the cause, her husband would not be able to keep it

---

[†]*slips.* counterfeit coins, apropos of the wife's having slipped, rendering her counterfeit.
[†]*dealt with her continually.* bawdy, with a pun on *continually.*

from her. And having now thoroughly instructed her, she dealt with her husband in this sort. One day when she knew him to be in his study alone, she came in to him and having fast locked the door after her and conveyed the key into her pocket, she began first with earnest entreaty and then with tears to crave that he would no longer keep from her the cause of his sudden alteration. The husband dissimuled[†] the matter still.

"At last she was so earnest to know for what cause he left money in such sort at sundry times that he answered on this wise. 'Wife, quod he, thou knowest how long we have been married together and how long I made so dear account of thee as ever man made of his wife. Since which days, thou knowest also how long I refrained thy company and how long again I have used thy company leaving the money in this sort, and the cause is this. So long as thou didst behave thyself faithfully towards me, I never loathed thy company, but sithens I have perceived thee to be a harlot and therefore did I for a time refrain and forbear to lie with thee. And now I can no longer forbear it, I do give thee every time that I lie with thee a slip, which is to make thee understand thine own whoredom. And this reward is sufficient for a whore.'

"The wife began stoutly to stand at defiance, but the husband cut off her speech and declared when, where, and how he had seen it. Hereat the woman being abashed, and finding her conscience guilty of as much as he had alleged, fell down on her knees and with most bitter tears craved pardon, confessing her offense. Whereat her husband, moved with pity, and melting likewise in floods of lamentation, recomforted her, promising that if from that day forwards she would be true unto him, he would not only forgive all

---

[†]*dissimuled.* gave the pretense of ignorance, dissembled.

that was past, but become more tender and loving unto her than ever he was.

"What do I tarry so long? They became of accord and in full accomplishment thereof, the gentlewoman did altogether eschew the company, the speech, and, as much as in her lay, the sight of her lover, although her husband did continue his courtesy towards him, and often charged his wife to make him fair semblant. The lover was now only left in perplexity, who knew nothing what might be the cause of all these changes and that most grieved him. He could by no means obtain again the speech of his desired. He watched all opportunities, he suborned messengers, he wrote letters, but all in vain.

"In the end she caused to be declared unto him a time and place where she would meet him and speak with him. Being met, she put him in remembrance of all that had passed between them. She laid also before him how trusty she had been unto him in all professions. She confessed also how faithfully he had discharged the duty of a friend in all respects and therewithal she declared that her late alteration and pensiveness of mind was not without great cause, for that she had of late such a mishap as might change the disposition of any living creature. Yea and that the case was such as unless she found present remedy, her death must needs ensue and that speedily for the preventing whereof, she alleged that she had beaten her brains with all devices possible, and that in the end she could think of no redress but one, the which lay only in him to accomplish. Wherefore she besought him for all the love and good will which passed between them, now to show the fruits of true friendship and to gratify her with a free grant to this request. The lover who had always been desirous to pleasure her in anything, but now especially to recover her wonted kindness, 'gan frankly promise to accomplish anything that might be to him possible, yea though it were to his great detriment and therewithal did deeply blame her in that she would so long torment herself with any grief, considering that it lay in him to help it.

"The lady answered that she had so long kept it from his knowledge because she doubted whether he would be contented to perform it or not, although it was such a thing as he might easily grant without any manner of hurt to himself and yet that now in the end she was forced to adventure upon his courtesy, being no longer able to bear the burden of her grief. The lover solicited her most earnestly to disclose it and she, as fast, seemed to mistrust that he would not accomplish it. In the end she took out a book, which she had brought for the nonce,[†] and bound him by oath to accomplish it. The lover mistrusting nothing less than that ensued, took the other willingly, which done, she declared all that had passed between her and her husband. His grief, her repentance, his pardon, her vow, and in the end of her tale enjoined the lover that from thence forthwards, he should never attempt to break her constant determination.

"The lover replied that this was unpossible, but she plainly assured him that if he granted her that request, she would be his friend in all honest and goodly wise. If not, she put him out of doubt that she would eschew his company and fly from his sight as from a scorpion. The lover considering that her request was but just, accusing his own guilty conscience, remembering the great courtesies always used by her husband and therewithal seeing the case now brought to such an issue as that by none other means than by this it could be concealed from knowledge of the world, but most of all, being urged by his oath, did at last give an unwilling consent and yet a faithful promise to yield unto her will in all things. And thus being become of one assent, he remaineth the dearest friend and most welcome guest

---

[†]*for the nonce.* for the express purpose; for the occasion.

that may be, both to the lady and her husband, and the man and wife so kind, each to other, as if there never had been such a breach between them.

"Now, of you noble governor, I would fain learn whether the perplexity of the husband when he looked in at the keyhole, or of the wife when she knew the cause why the slips were so scattered, or of the lover when he knew what was his mistress' charge, was greater of the three? I might have put in also the troubled thoughts of the sisters and the maid, when they saw their good will rejected, but let these three suffice."

"Gentle Hope," quod F.J., "you have rehearsed, and that right eloquently, a notable tale, or rather a notable history because you seem to affirm that it was done indeed of late and not far hence. Wherein I note five especial points: that is a marvelous patience in the husband, no less repentance in the wife, no small boldness of the maid, but much more rashness in the sisters, and last of all, a rare tractability in the lover. Nevertheless to return unto your question, I think the husband's perplexity greatest because his losses abounded above the rest and his injuries were uncomparable."

The Lady Frances did not seem to contrary him, but rather smiled in her sleeve at Dame Pergo, who had no less patience to hear the tale recited than the Lady Frances had pleasure in telling of it, but I may not rehearse the cause why, unless I should tell all.[†]

By this time the sleeping hour approached and the ladies prepared their departure, whenas Mistress Frances said unto F.J.: "Although percase I shall not do it so handsomely as your mistress, yet good Trust," quod she, "if you vouch-

---

[†]*unless I should tell all.* another potent indication that the novel concerns real people, and moreover that G.T. and F.J. are one and the same.

safe it, I can be content to trim up your bed in the best manner that I may, as one who would be as glad as she to procure your quiet rest."

F.J. gave her great thanks, desiring her not to trouble herself but to let his man alone with that charge. Thus they departed and how all parties took rest that night I know not. But in the morning F.J. began to consider with himself that he might lie long enough in his bed before his mistress would be appeased in her peevish conceits. Wherefore he arose and being appareled in his nightgown, took occasion to walk in the gallery near adjoining unto his mistress' chamber but there might he walk long enough ere his mistress would come to walk with him.

When dinnertime came he went into the great chamber where, as the Lord of the castle saluted him being joyful of his recovery, F.J. giving due thanks declared that his friendly entertainment together with the great courtesy of the gentlewomen was such as might revive a man, although he were half dead.

"I would be loath," quod the host, "that any gentleman coming to me for good will should want any courtesy of entertainment that lieth in my power."

When the meat was served to the table, the gentlewomen came in, all but Dame Elynor and Mistress Pergo, the which F.J. marked very well, and it did somewhat abate his appetite. After dinner, his Hope came unto him and demanded of him how he would pass the day for his recreation, to whom he answered even as it best pleased her. She devised to walk into the park and so, by little and little, to acquaint himself with the air, he agreed, and they walked together being accompanied with one or two other gentlewomen.

Here, less you should grow in some wrong conceit of F.J., I must put you out of doubt, that although there were now more cause that he should mistrust his mistress than ever he[†] had before received, yet the vehement passions which he saw in her when she first came to visit him and moreover the earnest words which she pronounced in his extremity were such a refreshing to his mind as that he determined no more to trouble himself with like conceits, concluding further that if his mistress were not faulty, then had he committed a foul offense in needless jealousy, and that if she were faulty, especially with the secretary, then no persuasion could amend her nor any passion help him. And this was the cause that enabled him after such passing pangs to abide the doubtful conclusion, thus manfully and valiantly to repress faintness of his mind, nothing doubting but that he should have won his mistress to pardon his presumption and lovingly to embrace his service in wonted manner.

But he was far deceived, for she was now in another town, the which Mistress Frances began partly to discover unto him as they walked together, for she burdened him that his malady proceeded only of a disquiet mind.

"And if it did so, my gentle Hope," quod he, "what remedy?"

"My good Trust," quod she, "none other but to plant quiet where disquiet began to grow."

"I have determined so," quod he, "but I must crave the help of your assurèd friendship."

"Thereof you may make account," quod she, "but wherein?"

F.J. walking apart with her began to declare that there was some contention happened between his mistress and him. The lady told him that she was not ignorant thereof.

[†]*ever he.* another play on the author's name, as witnessed on page 8.

Then he desired her to treat so much in the cause as they[†] might eftsoons come to parley.[†]

"Thereof I dare assure you," quod Mistress Frances, and at their return she led F.J. into his mistress' chamber, whom they found lying on her bed, whether galded with any grief or weary of the thing—which you woote[†] of—I know not, but there she lay, unto whom F.J. gave two or three salutations before she seemed to mark him.

At last said the Lady Frances unto her: "Your servant hearing of your sickness hath adventured thus far into the air to see you."

"I thank him," quod Dame Elynor, and so lay still, refusing to give him any countenance,[†] whereat F.J. perceiving all the other gentlewomen fall to whispering thought good boldly to plead his own case, and approaching the bed, began to enforce his unwilling mistress unto courtesy, wherein he used such vehemence as she could not well by any means refuse to talk with him, but what their talk was I may not take upon me to tell you unless you would have me fill up a whole volume only with his matters, and I have dilated them over largely already.

Sufficeth this to be known, that in the end she pretended to pass over all old grudges and thenceforth to pleasure him as occasion might serve, the which occasion was so long in happening that in the end F.J., being now eftsoons troubled with unquiet fantasies and forced to use his pen again as an ambassador between them, one day amongst the rest found opportunity to thrust a letter in her bosom, wherein he had earnestly requested another moonshine banquet or Friday's

---

[†]*as they.* so that they, i.e. F.J. and Elinor.
[†]*parley.* talk.
[†]*woote.* know; cognate with modern German *wesen,* 'to know', or for that matter with modern English *wise, wit,* and *witch.*
[†]*refusing to give him any countenance.* with a play on **count**enance, confirmed by the familiar phrase *his own case* following.

breakfast to recomfort his dullèd spirits, whereunto the dame yielded this answer in writing, but of whose indicting judge you.

G.T.

I can but smile at your simplicity,
Who burden your friend with an impossibility.
The case so stood
as I could not
though I would.
Wherefore from henceforth, either learn to frame your request more reasonably, or else stand content with a flat repulse. SHE.

F.J. liked this letter but a little, and being thereby driven into his accustomed vein, he compiled in verse this answer following, upon these words contained in her letter—*I could not though I would.*

G.T.

I could not though I would: good Lady say not so,
Since one good word of your good will might soon redress my woe,
Where 'would' is free before, there 'could' can never fail.
For proof, you see how galleys pass where ships can bear no sail,
The weary mariner when skies are overcast,
By ready will doth guide his skill and wins the haven[†] *at last;*
The pretty bird[†] *that sings with prick*[†] *against her breast*
Doth make a virtue of her need to watch when others rest.
And true the proverb is, which you have laid apart,
There is no hap can seem too hard unto a willing heart.

[†]*wins the haven.* often used to express sexual conquest, confirmed as such by the material discussed in connection with the next footnotes.
[†]*the pretty bird.* the nightingale, thought to pass the night with a thorn at her breast so as to remain awake and vigilant.
[†]*prick.* the thorn mentioned in the previous note but also a plausible play on the penis, as confirmed in the editorial essay following.

Then lovely Lady mine, you say not as you should,
In doubtful terms to answer thus: I could not though I would.
Yes, yes, full well you know, your 'can' is quick and good,
And willful 'will' is eke[†] too swift to shed my guiltless blood.
But if good will were bent as pressed as power is,
Such will would quickly find the skill to mend that is amiss.
Wherefore if you desire to see my true love spilt,
Command and I will slay myself, that yours may be the guilt.
But if you have no power to say your servant nay,
Write thus: I may not as I would, yet must I as I may.

F. J.

Thus F.J. replied upon his mistress' answer, hoping thereby to recover some favor at her hands, but it would not be. So that now he had been as likely, as at the first, to have fretted in fantasies, had not the Lady Frances continually comforted him. And by little and little she drove such reason into his mind that now he began to subdue his humors with discretion, and to determine that if he might espy evident proof of his mistress' frailty, he would then stand content with patience perforce[†] and give his mistress the *bezo las manos.*

And it happened one day amongst others that he resorted to his mistress' chamber and found her, *allo solito,*[†] lying upon her bed and the secretary with Dame Pergo, and her handmaid keeping of her company, where F.J. somewhat repining came to her and fell to dalliance as one that had now rather adventure to be thought presumptuous than yield to be accounted bashful, he cast his arm over his mistress and began to accuse her of sluggishness, using some

---

[†]*eke.* also.

[†]*patience perforce.* as found in the following line of one of Oxford's poems: **Patience perforce** *is such a pinching pain;* the phrase *pinching pain* is typically Shakespearean, as emphasized by J. Thomas Looney.

[†]*allo solito.* as usual; modern Italian *al solito,* the latter form being the past participle of *solere,* 'to be accustomed'.

other bold parts as well to provoke her, as also to grieve the other.

The Lady seemed little to delight in his dallying, but cast a glance at her secretary and therewith smiled, whenas the secretary and Dame Pergo burst out into open laughter, the which F.J. perceiving and disdaining her ingratitude was forced to depart and in that fantasy compiled this sonnet.

G.T.

> *With her in arms that had my heart in hold,*
> *I stood of late to plead for pity so,*
> *And as I did her lovely looks behold,*
> *She cast a glance upon my rival foe.*
> *His fleering face provokèd her to smile,*
> *When my salt tears were drownèd in disdain;*
> *He glad, I sad,[†] he laughed, alas the while,*
> *I wept for woe; I pined for deadly pain.*
>
> *And when I saw none other boot prevail,*
> *But reason's rule must guide my skillful mind;*
> *Why then, quod I, old proverbs never fail,*
> *For yet was never good cat out of kind.[†]*
>
> *Nor woman true but even as stories tell,*
> *Won with an egg and lost again with shell.[†]*
>
> *F. J.*

[†]*He glad, I sad.* with affinity to language appearing under the Earl of Oxford's signature:

> *They poor, I rich, they beg, I give,*
> *They lack, I leave, they pine, I live.*

[†]*never good cat out of kind.* perhaps a twist on the proverb *the cat is out of kind that sweet milk will not lap,* cf. Tilley [1950: C167]. Here the cat is F.J., denoted by *ever,* i.e. the author E. Vere. We may infer that F.J.'s milk was not sweet.

[†]*Won with ...shell.* easy come, easy go.

This sonnet declareth that he began now to account of her as she deserved, for it hath a sharp conclusion, and it is somewhat too general. Well, as it is he lost it where his mistress found it, and she immediately imparted the same unto Dame Pergo and Dame Pergo unto others, so that it quickly became common in the house. Amongst others, Mistress Frances, having recovered a copy of it, did seem to pardon the generality and to be well pleased with the particularity thereof, the which she bewrayed one day unto F.J. in this wise.

"Of all the joys that ever I had, my good Trust," quod she, "there is none wherein I take more comfort than in your conformity. And although your present rage is such that you can be content to condemn a number unknown for the transgression of one too well known, yet I do rather rejoice that you should judge your pleasure over many than to be abused by any."

"My good Hope," quod he, "it were not reason that after such manifold proofs of your exceeding courtesies, I should use strange or contentious speech with so dear a friend, and indeed I must confess that the opinion which I have conceived of my mistress hath stirred my pen to write very hardly[†] against all the feminine gender. But I pray you pardon me," quod he, "and if it please you I will recant it as also, percase, I was but cloyed with surquedry[†] and presumed to think more than may be proved."

"Yea, but how if it were proved?" quod Dame Frances.

"If it were so, which God forbid," quod he, "then could you not blame me to conceive that opinion."

"Howsoever I might blame you," quod she, "I mean not to blame you, but I demand further: if it be as I think and you suspect, what will you then do?"

[†]*stirred my pen ... hardly against.* bawdy with respect to *pen* and *hard.*
[†]*surquedry.* pride, arrogance; used in connection with excessive sex.

"Surely," quod F.J., "I have determined to drink up mine own sorrow secretly and to bid them both *a Dieu*."

"I like your farewell better than your fantasy," quod she, "and when soever you[†] can be content to take so much pains as the knight—which had a nightgown guarded with naked swords—did take, I think you may put yourself out of doubt of all these things."

By these words and other speech which she uttered unto him, F.J. smelt how the world went about and therefore did one day in the gray morning adventure to pass through the gallery towards his mistress' chamber, hoping to have found the door open, but he found the contrary and there attending in good devotion, heard the parting of his mistress and her secretary with many kind words. Whereby it appeared that the one was very loath to depart from the other. F.J. was enforced to bear this burden and after he had attended there as long as the light would give him leave, he departed also to his chamber, and appareling himself, could not be quiet until he had spoken with his mistress, whom he burdened flatly with this despiteful treachery. And she as fast denied it until at last being still urged with such evident token as he alleged, she gave him this bone to gnaw upon.

"And if I did so," quod she, "what then?"

Whereunto F.J. made none answer, but departed with this farewell:

"My loss is mine own, and your gain is none of yours, and sooner can I recover[†] my loss than you enjoy[†] the gain which you gape[†] after."

[†]*soever you.* a plausible play on the author's title and name, again identifying him with our protagonist F.J.

[†]*recover.* mount again; the reading is made plausible by what follows (as clarified in the next two notes) and by common usage of the verb *cover* for bestial copulation, extended by Shakespeare: *you'll have your daughter covered with a Barbary horse;* the Barbary horse is Othello and the daughter, Desdemona.

And when he was in place solitary, he compiled these
following for a final end of the matter.
G. T.

And if I did what then?
Are you agrieved therefore?
The sea hath fish for every man,†
And what would you have more?

Thus did my mistress once,
Amaze my mind with doubt:
And popped a question for the nonce,
To beat my brains about.

Whereto I thus replied,
Each fisherman can wish,
That all the sea at every tide,
Were his alone to fish.

And so did I, in vain,
But since it may not be,
Let such fish there as find the gain,
And leave the loss for me.

And with such luck and loss†
I will content myself;

---

†*enjoy.* take sexual pleasure, a reading made clear by the information
included in the previous and next note.
†*gape.* associated with the vagina, often in the context of whoredom;
Williams [1994:580] supplies related examples: (1576) *a man should
not ... consume his lusty years in haunting the company of whores, who
greedily gape;* and less subtly: (1697) *make all pricks to stand and
cunts to gape.*
†*every man.* E. Vere man.
†*luck and loss.* on this and related expressions, cf. Chapter 16 of *Shakespeare's Fingerprints.*

Till tides of turning time may toss,
Such fishers on the shelf.

And when they stick on sands,
That every man[†] *may see:*
Then will I laugh and clap my hands,
As they do now at me.
                    F.J.

It is time now to make an end of this thriftless history, wherein although I could wade much further, as to declare his departure, what thanks he gave to his Hope, &c., yet I will cease as one that had rather leave it unperfect than make it too plain. I have passed it over with *quod he* and *quod she* after my homely manner of writing, using sundry names for one person, as the *Dame*, the *Lady*, *Mistress*, &c, *the Lord of the castle*, *the Master of the house*, and *the host*. Nevertheless, for that I have seen good authors term every gentlewoman a lady and every gentleman *Domine*,[†] I have thought it no greater fault than petty treason thus to intermingle them, nothing doubting but you will easily understand my meaning, and that is as much as I desire.

[†]*every man.* a final covert reference to the author.
[†]*Domine.* Lord.

SECRET SHAKESPEARE'S SECRET IDENTITY

A sober reading of the adventures recounted in the foregoing novel should foster in the sensitive reader a strong sense of a *roman à clef*. Such a reaction is attested by the orthodox scholar Prouty, who in 1942 claimed that the anonymous author left behind clues "to the fact that the story does concern real people." To bolster his claim, he cited this passage from the novel:

> A gentlewoman of the company whom I have not
> hitherto named, and that for good respects, lest her name
> might altogether disclose the rest, 'gan thus propound:

A second extract from the novel also supports the conclusion. In it the author confesses that Pergo had a natural name, a transparent hint that a real name was involved.

> This dame had stuff in her, an old courtier, and a wily
> wench, whom for this discourse I will name Pergo, lest her
> name natural were too broad before, and might not drink
> of all waters.

Following on the obvious inference that the novel's actors were drawn from England's aristocracy, if we are to successfully identify the Elizabethan prototypes for F.J., Elinor, her secretary, Francis, Dame Pergo, and the Lord of the castle, we should be willing to explore the author's identity with an open mind, remaining cognizant of the fact that pseudonymity and wordplay were widely employed as literary devices within the timeframe of the novel's appearance and dissemination.

Several kinds of evidence confirm that Shakespeare was indeed the author, not only of the novel but more generally of the volume comprising it, namely *A Hundreth Sundrie Flowres,* hereafter abbreviated *Flowers.* For expediency, relevant categories of evidence are subsumed under the following taxonomy in what follows.

> *a. Relational fingerprints*
> *b. Wordplay and bawdry*
> *c. Elements of empirical confirmation*
> *d. Margination*

More often than not these topics intersect, as the reader will discover as the exposition unfolds. Indeed, topic (*c*) of section (4) will be seen to comprehend a number of examples of wordplay, all involving fingerprint evidence, and evidence turning on another species of wordplay, what we term *margination*, is provided in the Appendix.

1. RELATIONAL FINGERPRINTS

If brushstrokes and musical scores can be used to identify artists and musicians, then certainly the language employed by authors incorporates clues to their identity. The Shakespearean connection with *Flowers* can be established by taking note of a set of relational fingerprints, many of which have been adduced in Chapters 9 and 12 of our earlier *Shakespeare's Fingerprints*. To provide a simple, yet convincing example of a diagnostic fingerprint, we may consider the congruence holding between a couplet drawn from Shakespeare's *Sonnet 123* and one found in the novel, the latter hereafter abbreviated *Freeman*.

SHAKESPEARE: *This **I** do vow **and** this **shall ever be**,*
*I will be true despite thy scythe and **thee**.*
Sonnet 123, 13-4.

FREEMAN: *Such one **I** was **and** such **always will be**,*
*For worthy dames, but then **I** mean not **thee**.*

Careful inspection and comparison of the two couplets reveals (*i*) impressive lexical overlap (as indicated by our interpolated boldface font), (*ii*) a nontrivial degree of syntactic relatedness, (*iii*) identical rhyme, and (*iv*) semantic overlap. Convergence of such congruence relations is indicative of a single creator and is what we intend when we employ the phrase *relational fingerprints*.

In more detail, the relational fingerprint we have just cited exhibits not only a striking case of 7-fold lexical overlap, those seven items bear identical relative sequential order across the two couplets. Of all the relational types important for authorship identification, *syntactic relatedness* must be counted among the most powerful. This type of congruence relation can be made more explicit in the instant case by invoking the following picture.

TOPIC 1	CLAUSE 1	CONJUNCTION	TOPIC 2	CLAUSE 2
Such one	*I was*	*and*	*such*	*always will be*
This	*I do vow*	*and*	*this*	*shall ever be*

Note that the topics are coreferential within their respective conjoined clauses: *such-such, this-this*. A further point of convergence suggesting identical authorship frames both couplets with rhyme incident to the ordered pair (*be, thee*). Thus, *be* is the rhyming word of the first line of both couplets and *thee,* the rhyming word of the second. Finally, the two couplets are semantically congruent, as both couplets express constancy. Now any one of these relations—those turning on lexicon, coreference, syntax, rhyme, or semantics—is suggestive, while convergence of all goes far towards empirically bearing out our claim that we are not dealing with some kind of random coincidence. It follows that one of the following propositions is true.

i. Shakespeare imitated the couplet found in *Freeman*.
ii. Shakespeare himself wrote *Freeman*.

Experience with literary detection suggests that such converging overlap is more reminiscent of genuine literary fingerprints than it is of plagiary. If imitation or plagiary were truly involved, we would not expect to find such subtle syntactic variance. Indeed, syntactic relatedness is one of the most reliable criteria for establishing pseudonymity.

As most lovers of good literature are aware, Shakespeare was a genius. Could it not then be that in spite of our criteria he was a syntactic copycat, i.e. a plagiarist? To adjust for false positives resulting from plagiary or imitation, we require that such evidence as we have adduced be supplemented to confirm a cumulative effect of converging congruence relations from whence it would emerge as highly unlikely that any man, even one of Shakespeare's caliber, would have taken the time and effort to plagiarize in such iteratively convergent fashion. To see this effect, we must adduce additional examples, of which one such is the following noted in the footnotes to the text proper.

FREEMAN: *So they that seek to break the links of* **love**
Strive with the stream **and this by** *pain* **I prove.**
$\cong_{LEX-6}, \cong_{RIME}, \cong_{SYN}$
SHAKESPEARE: *Came there for cure,* **and this by** *that* **I prove,**
Love's fire heats water, water cools not **love.**
Sonnet 154, 13-4.

Here is an example of 6-fold lexical congruence buttressed by identical rhyme, indicated by drawing on the relational symbol '$\cong$' and specialized by subscripts, so that '$\cong_{LEX}$' denotes the special case of lexical relatedness, $\cong_{RIME}$ the relation of rhyme congruence. We also refine the notation, signaling valence with a subscript. Since six lexical items are involved in the above example, the augmented symbol '$\cong_{LEX-6}$' is employed. We will mark additional relations with analogous symbols. Thus, in the above example we witness a notable degree of syntactic overlap. The evidence clearly converges to suggest one and the same author, and it is this kind of accumulation—the above example with the former and with a plentitude of others—that indubitably identifies our author as the celebrated poet and playwright William Shakespeare.

Accumulation is thus seen to hold across *Freeman* and Shakespeare's glorious sonnets, but it is also witnessed in connection with examples drawn from additional works attributed to the great poet-playwright. A wealth of such evidence is adduced in *Shakespeare's Fingerprints,* including fingerprints such as the following.

FREEMAN: *Thou with thy looks* <u>*on whom I look*</u> **full** *oft,*
And find therein great cause of deep delight:
Thy **face** *is fair,* **thy** *skin is smooth and* **soft,**
Thy **lips** *are* **sweet, thine eyes** *are clear and bright,*

$\cong_{LEX-8}, \cong_{SEM}, \cong_{SYN}$
SHAKESPEARE: *Alas, he naught esteems that* **face** *of* **thine,**
<u>*To which love's eyes pays tributary gazes;*</u>
Nor **thy soft** *hands,* **sweet lips** *and crystal* **eyne,**
Whose **full** *perfection all the world amazes:*
Venus and Adonis, 631-4

This example features an 8-fold lexical congruence in conjunction with similar syntax and semantics. Thus, it too is symptomatic of something far deeper than random coincidence. That something, we reiterate, relates to authorship. Here too relational fingerprints provide us with a cogent argument showing that it is proposition (*ii*) cited above rather than (*i*) that explains the accumulation of the converging congruences uncovered.

That a single author is truly indicted is confirmed by the fact that many more examples accumulate to support what we have elsewhere called the *cascade effect* of relational fingerprints. Thus, when we consider the above four lines drawn from Shakespeare, we may also notice that the image involving eyes and gazing cascades back to the verse of *Freeman*.

SHAKESPEARE: *To which love's **eyes** pays tributary **gazes;***
         Venus and Adonis, 632.

FREEMAN: *What will you more? So oft, my **gazing eyes** did seek*

The tenor of this Shakespearean example is precisely what we find in the example drawn from *Freeman.* When we extend our forensic methods to all of *Flowers,* we find many convincing examples of cascade. To wit, in the following illustration we encounter examples cascading from Shakespeare's *Sonnet 130* to the verse of *Flowers* and back again to Shakespeare's *Henry V.*

SHAKESPEARE: *My mistress' **eyes** <u>are nothing</u> **like the sun**;*
         Coral is far more red than her lips' red;
         If snow be white, why then her breasts are dun;
         *If **hairs** be **wires**, black wires grow on **her head**.*
             Sonnet 130, 1-4

             $\cong$*LEX-8*, $\cong$*SYN*, $\cong$*FIG-2*
FLOWERS: *First for **her head**, the **hairs** <u>were not of gold</u>,*
       But of some other metal far more fine,
       Whereof each crinet seemèd to behold,
       *Like glist'ring **wires** against **the sun** that shine,*
       *And therewithal the blazing of her **eyne**,*
       *Was **like** the beams of <u>Titan</u>, truth to tell,*
       Which glads us all that in this world do dwell.
       Which flinging fault, because it is not new,
       *Nor seldom seen in **kites of Cresside's kind**,*
       I marvel not, nor bear it much in mind.
             Flowers, 152.

$$\cong_{LEX-4}$$

SHAKESPEARE: The lazar **kite of Cressid's kind**
Henry V. ii. 1.

The first relation involves two related metaphors, accounting for
the symbol '$\cong_{FIG-2}$'. Additional lines supporting an accumulation of
cascading congruences could easily be cited. The sum of such examples again confirms that *Flowers,* and hence the novel it contains, is a work written, not plagiarized, by the genius we today
know as William Shakespeare.

One obvious problem with our conclusion must be confronted
without equivocation. We recall that the traditional Shakespeare
was born in Stratford in 1564, while *Flowers* was written no later
than 1572, rolling off the press in 1573. The apparent problem is
that William of Stratford was a lad of eight years in 1572 and hence
too young to have written much of the artistically bawdy prose
found in *Freeman.* Moreover, he was inexperienced and isolated
and thus hardly had the knowledge prerequisite to the writing of a
masterwork like *Flowers.* For example, it is doubtful that an eight-
year-old commoner from Stratford could have written the bawdy
sonnet of which the following is but one representative quatrain.

> *As some men say there is a kind of seed*
> *Will grow to horns if it be sowèd thick:*
> *Wherewith I thought to try if I could breed*
> *A brood of buds, well sharpèd in the prick:*

This manner of verse would have been exceedingly bold for any
Elizabethan poet (and for publishers alike). What makes *Freeman* a
particularly gutsy production is not its wanton character per se, but
rather the conjunction of bawdy verse with poetry linkable to Queen
Elizabeth.

> ***Dame Cynthia** herself, that **shines** so bright,*
> *And deigneth not to leave her lofty place:*
> *But only then when Phoebus shows his face*
> *Which is her brother born and lends her light,*

The name *Cynthia* is an alternative epithet for Diana, virgin
goddess of the hearth and hunt. Inasmuch as Queen Elizabeth was

billed a virgin, poets commonly referred to her as *Cynthia* and *Diana*. Shakespeare evinces the same symbolism, more evidence for our thesis that we are dealing with one and the same author.

> **Cynthia** _for shame_ obscures her silver **shine**,
> *Venus and Adonis, 728.*

Presence of both **Cynthia** and **shine** provides significant overlap with the *Freeman* poem, but when we continue with the *Freeman* poem, we encounter the exact same phrase as that underscored a-bove, providing a more potent argument still for a unique author.

> *The courteous* **Moon** *that wished to do me good,*
> *Did shine to show my dame more perfectly,*
> *But when she saw her passing jollity,*
> *The* **Moon** _for shame_ *did blush as red as blood,*
> *And shrunk aside and kept her horns in hood:*
> *So that now when* **Dame Cynthia** *was gone,*
> *I might enjoy my lady's looks alone,*
> *Yet honored still the* **Moon** *with true intent:*
> *Who taught us skill,*
> *To work our will,*
> *And gave us place till all the night was spent.*

Since the moon was the heavenly aspect of Diana, it too was em-braced as a means of referring to the Tudor monarch. In this context it is interesting to note that the poem terminates with an erotic sug-gestion. Indeed, the phrase *to work our will* includes a bawdy reading and almost any man placing the Queen within such a context would have found himself in the unenviable position of an-ticipating loss of a hand by an executioner's axe, if not a head. So apart from the early publication date of *Flowers,* we find that the author's bawdy verse provides motivation for dismissing the tradi-tional commoner from Stratford as its author, as also the alleged soldier George Gascoigne. This dismissal raises the question of how we might resolve the dilemma that now confronts us: on the one hand linguistic considerations confirm that Shakespeare wrote the *Freeman Jones* novel; on the other, due to age considerations the man from Stratford could not have written it.

If we refer to the Stratford man as William of Stratford, then the inference is simply that William of Stratford did not write the *Freeman* novel, from whence it follows that he also did not write the great plays and poems associated with the name *William Shakespeare*. In other words, someone other than William of Stratford was the genuine author of the greatest literature ever written in the English language. It follows that the name *William Shakespeare* is a pseudonym for someone who could afford to be so bold as to jest with the Queen, perhaps by way of entertaining her. Such an individual would have necessarily been close to the sovereign, perhaps a favorite. Who might that genius have been?

The last question is approachable from various directions. We might look to the Elizabethan Court for some outstanding poet and novelist recognized as such in his own lifetime. The problem with such a tack is that our mystery man kept his identity as an author in large part hidden (although there are some explicit clues to who was best at court, provided in Chapter 4 of *Shakespeare's Fingerprints*).

Another strategy that clearly suggests itself is that of looking to the formal properties of language in the hope of anchoring emergent fingerprints in some known Elizabethan courtier. Without going into detail, we note that relational fingerprints such as the following indict Edward de Vere 17th Earl of Oxford as the creator of *Flowers* and hence of the novel we are here calling *Freeman*.

DE VERE: *The laboring man that tills the fertile soil,*
         *And **reaps** the harvest **fruit**, hath not in deed*
         *The **gain**, but **pain**; and if for all his toil*
         He gets the straw, the lord will have the seed.

$$\cong_{LEX\text{-}4}, \cong_{FIG}$$

FLOWERS:

But since my luckless lot forbids me now to taste,
*The dulcet **fruits** of my delight, therefore in woes I waste.*
And swallow-like I sing, as one enforcèd so,
*Since others **reap** the **gainful** crop, which I with **pain** did sow.*

Upon inspection of these lines, we find congruence with respect to both form and content. That is, not only do we encounter an impressive example of lexical overlap, we also witness a convergence with respect to metaphor and meaning. Both de Vere and the author of *Freeman* are talking about the same thing in related metaphors.

Such confluence of form and content is hardly a fluke to be blamed on random coincidence.

Henceforth, when we provide citations drawn from de Vere's poems, we will append what we choose to call its *May-number,* which is just the number the orthodox scholar Stephen May provided in his 1980 article to refer to a poem that he accepted as definitely a work created by Edward de Vere. We may proceed by citing additional fingerprints contributing to the cumulative evidence showing that de Vere was indeed the mystery man behind *Flowers.*

DE VERE: *For **he** that **beats the bush the bird** not gets,*
          *But who sits **still** and holdeth fast the nets.*
                    May-1.

             $\cong_{LEX-7}$, $\cong_{FIG}$, $\cong_{SEM}$
DE VERE:

*And **he** that **beats the bush, the** wishèd **bird** not gets,*
*But such I see as sitteth **still**, and holds the fowling nets.*
                    May-2.

             $\cong_{LEX-7}$, $\cong_{FIG}$, $\cong_{SEM}$
FLOWERS:

He bet** about **the bush,** whiles other caught **the birds,
*Whom crafty Cresside mocked too much, yet fed him **still** with words.*

The impressive accumulation of such examples of converging congruences lends credence to the argument for de Vere's authorship of *Flowers,* while yet another example involving a slightly different convergence of congruence types, including rhyme congruence, confirms it beyond reasonable doubt.

DE VERE:

*Of **all** that may in heaven or hell, in earth or air be **found,***
*To wail with **me** this loss of mine, as of these griefs **the ground**.*
                    May-4.

             $\cong_{LEX-5}$, $\cong_{RIME}$
FREEMAN: *And **me** even now, thy gall hath so infect,*
              *As **all** the joys which ever lover **found,***
              And all good haps, that ever Troilus' sect,
              *Achievèd yet above **the** luckless **ground**:*

Here we encounter a 5-fold congruence relation that cannot be blamed on commonplaces, while the addition of rhyme congruence and semantic congruence adds more confirmation. Many more such examples could be added, among which the following is of some interest.

FREEMAN:
*At last her worthy will would **pity** this **my plaint**,*
*And comfort **me** her own poor slave, whom fear had make so faint.*

$\cong_{LEX-4}$
DE VERE: *The more **my plaints** I do resound*
*The less she **pities me**;*
The more I sought the less I found,
Yet mine she meant to be.
May-3.

The relevance of syntactic congruence becomes more obvious when we proceed to investigate more of de Vere's poetry.

DE VERE:
*My meaning is to work <u>what wonders **love hath** wrought</u>,*
*Wherewith I muse why men of wit have **love so dearly bought**;*
May-7, 1-2.

$\cong_{LEX-6}$, $\cong_{SYN}$
FLOWERS:
*Yet for a just reward of **love so dearly bought**,*
*I pray you say, lo this was he, <u>whom **love had** worn to naught</u>.*

The embedded *wh*-clauses, headed by *what* in one example and by *whom* in the other, both include the word *love* as subject. This convergence is hardly accidental within the context of the ambient repetition of the phrase *love so dearly bought*.

A poetic device known by the technical name *anaphora* can be brought to bear to support our demonstration. This device is characterized by repetition of lexical items at the beginning (or near-beginning) of poetic lines and provides us with a new source of converging evidence, involving lexicon and syntax. In this connection we witness cascade from *Flowers* to de Vere and then back to *Flowers* in the following extracts.

FLOWERS: ***And** canst thou now condemn his loyalty?*
***And** canst thou craft to flatter such a friend?*
***And** canst thou see him sink in jeopardy?*
***And** canst thou seek to bring his **life** to end?*
Flowers.

$\cong_{LEX\text{-}5}, \cong_{ANA}, \cong_{SYN}$

DE VERE: ***And shall I** live on earth to be her thrall?*
***And shall I live** and serve her all in vain?*
***And** kiss the steps that she lets fall,*
***And** shall **I** pray the Gods to keep the pain*
May-9, 25-8.

$\cong_{ANA}, \cong_{LEX\text{-}8}, \cong_{SYN}$

FLOWERS:
***And** you **shall** know the cause, wherefore these robes are worn,*
***And** why **I** go outlandish-like, yet being English born.*
***And** why **I** thus presume, to press into this place,*
***And** why **I**, simple boy, am bold to look such men in face.*

The syntactic evidence linking *Flowers* with de Vere is indicated by our usual convention of underlining. Should anaphoric congruence in this case strike the reader as too common, then additional examples involving different items could be cited, including comparisons such as the following.

FLOWERS:
***Who** in my danger's deep did deign to do me good,*
***Who** did relieve **my** heavy **heart** and sought to save my blood,*
***Who first** increased my friends and overthrew my foes,*
***Who** loved all them that wished me well and likèd none but those?*

$\cong_{ANA\text{-}4}, \cong_{LEX\text{-}7}, \cong_{SYN}$

DE VERE:
***Who** taught thee **first** to sigh, alas, **my heart**?*
***Who** taught thy tongue the woeful words of plaint?*
***Who** filled your eyes with tears of bitter smart?*
***Who** gave thee grief and made thy joys to faint?*
May 15, 1-4.

The identical 4-fold anaphoric congruence inhering in this fingerprint converges with the inclusion of additional lexical items, including ***first*** and ***my*** ... ***heart***. This convergence in turn provides a new argument for linking the poetry of *Flowers* with that of de Vere. Such examples showcasing all these properties are of singular interest because they involve nothing that could be construed as "commonplace" or convention. Another fingerprint devoid of anything that could be called common property is also gleaned from our page 30.

FREEMAN:
> *And smiling yet __full oft__, __I have beheld that face__,*
> *When in my heart I might bewail mine own unlucky case:*
> ***And** oft again with looks that **might** bewray my grief,*
> *I pleaded **hard** for just reward and sought to find relief.*

$$\cong_{LEX-5}, \cong_{SYN}, \cong_{SEM}$$

DE VERE:
Yet for the day was calm and clear __I might discern her face__,
As one might see a damask rose hid under crystal glass.
Three times with her soft hand __full hard__ on her left side she knocks,
***And** sighed so sore as **might** have moved some pity in the rocks:*

Based on this and much additional relational evidence, we conclude that Edward de Vere was the author of *Flowers,* and hence of *Freeman.* In view of the earlier evidence, this conclusion in turn implies that the man behind the *Shakespeare* pseudonym was in fact de Vere.

We now emerge with an interesting prediction: de Vere's attested fingerprints should match Shakespeare's. That this is precisely what we find when we consult the relevant literature confirms the strong claim to Oxford's authorship.

To disclose the evidence in more detail, we will focus for the moment on bestial metaphors, or what we have elsewhere dubbed *companimality,* for which we utilize the special symbol '$\cong_{COM}$'.

DE VERE:
> *The swiftest hare unto the mastive **slow***
> *Oft times doth fall, to him as for a **prey**;*
> *The grey**hound** thereby doth miss his game we know*
> *For which he made such **speedy** haste away.*
>   *May-1.*

$\cong$*LEX-4* , $\cong$*COM*

SHAKESPEARE:
> *Look as the full-fed* **hound** *or gorgèd hawk,*
> *Unapt for tender smell or* **speedy** *flight,*
> *Make* **slow** *pursuit, or altogether balk*
> *The* **prey** *wherein by nature they delight:*
> *Rape of Lucrece, 694-7.*

And turning now from hounds to drones:

DE VERE: *The idle* **drone** *that labors not at all,*
> **Sucks** *up the sweet of* **honey** *from the* **bee;**
> *Who worketh most to their share least doth fall,*
> *With due desert reward will never be.*
> *May-1, 13-6.*

$\cong$*COM* , $\cong$*LEX-4* , $\cong$*SEM*

SHAKESPEARE: *My honey lost, and I a* **drone**-*like bee,*
> *Have no perfection of my summer left,*
> *But robbed and ransacked by injurious theft;*
> *In thy weak hive a wand'ring wasp hath crept,*
> *And* **sucked** *the* **honey** *which thy chaste* **bee** *kept.*
> *Rape of Lucrece.*

Pursuing the drone further, we encounter the following example of 4-fold lexical overlap.

SHAKESPEARE: *Good Helicane hath stayed at home,*
> **Not** *to eat* **honey** *like a* **drone**
> *From others'* **labors***; for though he strive*
> *To killen bad, keep good alive;*
> *And to fulfill his prince desire,*
> *Sends word of all that haps in Tyre:*
> *Pericles, 2, Epilogue.*

$\cong$*COM* , $\cong$*LEX-4*

DE VERE: *The idle* **drone** *that* **labors not** *at all,*
> *Sucks up the sweet of* **honey** *from the bee;*
> *Who worketh most to their share least doth fall,*
> *With due desert reward will never be.*
> *Labor and Its Reward, May-1.*

Indeed, a cascade of converging fingerprints is evident from de Vere to Shakespeare and back again to de Vere.

DE VERE:
> *The drone more honey sucks, that laboreth not at all,*
> *Than doth the bee, to whose most pain, least pleasure doth befall;*
> *May-2.*

$\cong_{COM}$, $\cong_{LEX-4}$

SHAKESPEARE:
> *Not to eat honey like a drone*
> *From others' labors; for though he strive*
> *Pericles, 2, Epilogue.*

$\cong_{COM}$, $\cong_{LEX-5}$

DE VERE:
> *The idle drone that labors not at all,*
> *Sucks up the sweet of honey from the bee;*
> *May-1.*

We also witness a cascade from Freeman to de Vere and from there to Shakespeare.

FREEMAN:
> *The greyhound is aggrieved, although he see his game,*
> *If still in slip he must be stayed, when he would chase the same.*
> *Flowers, 59.*

$\cong_{COM}$, $\cong_{LEX-5}$, $\cong_{SEM}$

DE VERE:
> *The swiftest hare unto the mastive slow*
> *Oft times doth fall, to him as for a prey;*
> *The greyhound thereby doth miss his game we know*
> *For which he made such speedy haste away.*
> *May-1, 17-20.*

$\cong_{COM}$, $\cong_{LEX-5}$, $\cong_{SEM}$

SHAKESPEARE:
> *Look as the full-fed hound or gorgèd hawk,*
> *Unapt for tender smell or speedy flight,*
> *Make slow pursuit, or altogether balk*
> *The prey wherein by nature they delight:*
> *Rape of Lucrece, 694-7.*

Alternatively, we may cascade from *Freeman* to Shakespeare and thence to de Vere with examples all illustrating the device of serialization of prepositional phrases.

FREEMAN: *But dead or live, **in heaven, in earth, in hell***
I will be thine where so my carcass dwell.
Freeman, 37.

$\cong_{LEX-6}, \cong_{SER}$

SHAKESPEARE: *Ant S.   Am I **in earth, in heaven, or in hell?***
Comedy of Errors, 2.2.

$\cong_{LEX-6}, \cong_{SER}$

DE VERE:
*Of all that may **in heaven or hell, in earth** or air be found,*
To wail with me this loss of mine, as of these griefs the ground.
May-4, 11-2.

J. Thomas Looney first provided fingerprint evidence identifying the name *William Shakespeare* as a pseudonym for Edward de Vere. As early as 1920 he noted the following example, which we will express here within our own notational framework.

SHAKESPEARE: ***Who taught thee how to** make me love thee more,*
Sonnet 150, 9.

$\cong_{LEX-5}, \cong_{SYN}, \cong_{ANA}$

DE VERE: ***Who taught thee how to** sigh alas, my heart?*
May-15, 1.

Another diagnostic fingerprint discovered by Looney includes an example involving significant lexical overlap converging with a remarkable semantic relatedness.

SHAKESPEARE: ***That** most **are** busied **when** they're most **alone.***
Romeo and Juliet 1.1.

$\cong_{LEX-5}, \cong_{SEM}, \cong_{SYN}$

DE VERE: ***That** never **am** less idle, lo, than **when I am alone.***
May-2, 18.

The idea expressed here goes back to Cicero, but that does not obviate the significance of the fact that it was de Vere who made copious use of it in his art. We may add to Looney's observations by noting the cascade from de Vere back to *Freeman*.

SHAKESPEARE: ***Who taught thee how to** make me love thee more,*
Sonnet 150, 9.

DE VERE: $\cong_{LEX-5}$, $\cong_{SYN}$, $\cong_{ANA}$
          Who taught thee how** to sigh alas, **my heart?
                              May-15.

FLOWERS: $\cong_{LEX-5}$, $\cong_{SYN}$, $\cong_{ANA}$
***Who** did relieve **my** heavy **heart** and sought **to** save **my** blood,*

The same type of relational result is obtainable with respect to the second Looney example.

SHAKESPEARE: ***That** most **are** busied **when** they're most **alone.***
                              Romeo and Juliet 1.1.

            $\cong_{LEX-5}$, $\cong_{SYN}$, $\cong_{SEM}$, $\cong_{ANA}$
DE VERE: ***That** never **am** less idle, lo, **than when I am alone.***
                              May-2, 18.

            $\cong_{LEX-5}$, $\cong_{SEM}$, $\cong_{SYN}$
FREEMAN: *Much worse I fear **than when I was alone.***
                              Flowers, 78.

The added comparison of de Vere with *Freeman* in the last case is particularly striking. Not only does the example support lexical congruence of a relatively high valence, it also features identical syntax with respect to the comparative clauses, which we have set off by underscoring. Added to all this is a similar mode of comparison in the main clauses in terms of the semantic congruence as *less idle* $\cong$ *worse*.

2. WORDPLAY AND BAWDRY

If de Vere was the author of our novel, we are in a position to understand why it was that he could get away with as much as he did without losing a hand or a head to a regal axe. Upon the death of his father in 1562, the youthful Edward had assumed the title of Earl of Oxford and as such he inherited the honorary title of Great Lord Chamberlain. If we add to his nobility and titles the fact that he possessed a fiercely independent mind, a huge ego, and more literary talent than the world has ever witnessed past or present, or is likely ever to witness in the future, and if we factor into the equation the fact that his father-in-law was the Lord High Treasurer and the power behind the Crown—characterized on the Continent as the

"King of England"—we are able to better comprehend why this nobleman was in a position to freely pursue his personal agenda of creating an English-based literature, indulging in bawdy references along the way.

Only one close to the Queen could have produced a volume comprising bawdy verse on the one hand and poems associated with the liege lady on the other. Indeed, some poems were harshly critical of her. It therefore makes sense that the author could only have been a nobleman.

Edward de Vere was such a nobleman, known to have written poems and plays of high quality, as we have documented in *Shakespeare's Fingerprints*. Equally important, he was known to have been the Queen's favorite prior to the publication of *Flowers*, as attested by a surviving letter from the nobleman Gilbert Talbot to his father.

> My Lord of Oxford is lately grown into great credit, for the Queen's Majesty delighteth more in his personage and his dancing and valiantness than any other.
> Gilbert Talbot, *letter of 1573.*

We also know from de Vere's subsequent life that he suffered repeated trials and tribulations at the hands of the Queen, as no doubt she also at his, leading to his multiple banishments from Court and at least two imprisonments in the Tower, a topic Oxford was to revisit in literature later published under the *Shakespeare* pseudonym, as in *Measure for Measure,* to mention but one play. Even in the same letter Talbot provides a foreboding of problems to come.

> I think Sussex doth back him [Oxford] all he can. If it were not for his fickle head he would pass any of them shortly.
> Gilbert Talbot, *letter of 1573.*

So the creation of *Flowers* squares well not only with internal fingerprint evidence, but also with external evidence relating to the personal life of the Earl of Oxford. Indeed, some of the poems in *Flowers* clearly show that the author was a nobleman. For example, that author writes of a court where princes reign, which can be none other than Queen Elizabeth's.

In court where princes reign, her place is now assigned.
And well were worthy for the room, if she were not unkind.

Crucially, he confides that he was present in that court:

There I in wonted wise did show myself of late,
And that as the soil was changed, so love was turned to hate.

Several lines later in the same poem, the author informs us that he has fallen out of grace.

And I since porters put me from my wonted place
*And deep deceit hath wrought a wile **to wrest me out of grace:***

We are inspired to ask: whose grace? The answer is obvious, or if not, it soon will be. Now the fact that we can bring a bounty of internal evidence to bear on the authorship question would seem to clinch the case for de Vere's authorship of *Flowers*. In particular, the 1573 publication comprising the *Freeman Jones* novel was revised, ostensibly in response to objections voiced by some exponents of the nobility who perceived that they were figured in it.

In the revised and expurgated version of the novel, the setting was moved from England to Italy, the English protagonist F.J. (or F.I.) became Ferdinando, and the name *Elinor* metamorphosed into the Italian name *Leonora*. More generally, *Flowers* was revised, reorganized, and retitled, with de Vere now appropriating a name from a real-life soldier and government agent to further distance himself from the original production. To bolster plausible deniability of authorship, the author included in the revision a specious claim to the effect that the novel was a translation from Italian.

The expurgated revision was retitled *The Posies of George Gascoigne Esquire,* including the motto *Tam Marti quam Mercurio,* which may be translated 'as Mars, so too Mercury', providing a potential element of misinformation for consumption by the unknowing reader. In other words, the author was to be perceived as both soldier and poet.

It is important to recognize that the real-life Gascoigne had served as a courier or 'carrier', a functionary in the service of the director of the Secret Service, Francis Walsingham.

"Paid upon a warrant signed by Mr. Secretaire Walsingham,
dated at Hampton Court xxj° Novembr. 1576, to George
Gascoigne, gent. for bringinge of Lettres in post for her
Ma[ties] affaires frome Andwarpe to Hampton Courte ... xx[li]
Revels Accounts, Cunningham [1842: *xxxi*]

The real-life Gascoigne was thereby intimately related to the
Tudor regime, a further clarification of the link extending to the
Treasurer's son-in-law, Edward de Vere, 17th Earl of Oxford.

2.1 Penis Play

Before commenting further on the *Gascoigne* pseudonym, we
are advised to return to Shakespeare with a view to considering his
bawdy verse. In this connection, the genius reveals his identity as
Oxford.

> *Wilt thou whose **will** is large and spacious,*
> *Not once vouchsafe to hide my **will** in thine,*
> *Shall **will** in others seem right gracious,*
> *And in my **will** no **fair** acceptance shine:*
> *Sonnet 135, 5-8.*

In this second quatrain of *Sonnet 135*, the great poet-playwright
makes it obvious that *will* and *Will* are puns on his and his mistress'
genitalia, and one easily recognizes that the word *fair* is a play on
the family name *Vere*. Now let us turn back to the novel, in particular to the poetic lines found on our page 31.

Then, all too late, aghast, I did my foot retire,
And sought with secret sighs to quench my greedy scalding fire:
*But lo, I did prevail as much **to guide my will**,*
As he that seeks with halting heel to hop against the hill.
Freeman.

Shakespeare's conveyance of the word *will* suggests that a similar bawdy nuance may inhere in the third line cited above. We have
said in a footnote that this interpretation is consistent with the discussion following within the text, beginning with the pun framed as
a *continua oratio*. We thus emerge with yet another point of contact

between Shakespeare and the author of *Freeman,* the latter of whom will be called Gascoigne, consistent with the later revision.

In his cleverly devious manner, our genius plays with a variety of words, all in the spirit of his own *will.* For another example, one senses in his use of *sword* a palpable phallic presence, an impression gleaned from a line uttered by Margaret to Benedict in *Much Ado About Nothing.*

> Give us the **swords**, we have **bucklers** of our own.
> *Much Ado About Nothing, 5.2.*

The contrast between swords and bucklers is figuratively one of masculinity and femininity, respectively, as suggested by the elongated and circular shapes associated respectively with swords and shields. It may not be for naught that Shakespeare named the protagonist of this comedy as he did, a name consisting of two stems, *Bene-dick*, the first translating as 'good' or 'well', the second by what all speakers of English know from childhood. Indeed, the name of the play may well be a bawdy inspiration, as no-

A courtier bears his sword. Was he Oxford as some scholars have claimed?

thing is the absence of something, while the male something includes anything having a potential sword-like presence, supplying a possible insight into the *nothing* of the title. These potential connections are noted in Chapter 0 of *Shakespeare's Fingerprints.*

Returning to *Freeman,* we find that Gascoigne displays a like mind when it comes to swords.

> And when he thought as well his servant as the rest of household to be safe, he arose again and, taking his nightgown, did under the same convey **his naked sword**, and so walked to the gallery, where he found his good mistress walking in her nightgown and attending his coming.

One senses that the lexical choice of *sword* is again a play on the male organ, exactly as we found in connection with Shakespeare in the last section, with the confirmatory lexical addition of *coming.*

Indeed, in this wonderful novel Oxford's point is driven home when Freeman and Elinor, after much foreplay, find occasion to requite their mutual desire.

> The moon was now at the full, the skies clear, and the weather temperate, by reason whereof he might the more plainly and with the greater contentation behold his long desired joys, and spreading his arms abroad to embrace his loving mistress, he said: "Oh my dear lady, when shall I be able with any desert to countervail the least part of this your bountiful goodness?"
>
> The dame, whether it were of fear in deed, or that the wiliness of womanhood had taught her to cover her conceits with some fine dissimulation, stert back from the knight and shrieking—but softly—said unto him: "Alas servant, what have I deserved that you come against me with **naked sword** as against an open enemy?"
>
> *Freeman, 43.*

The phrase *open enemy* relates to Elinor's propensity to receive, with the noun *enemy* an illustration of the literary tradition of *militia amoris*, the device of relating lovemaking to war, and hence the beloved to the enemy. In a similar vein, the phrases *come against me* and *attending his coming* are unmistakable examples of sexual play from which we conclude that the author of *Freeman*, like Shakespeare, was a prankster who reveled in wanton wordplay. This convergence, to be sure, is no accident, as the wordplay in *Freeman* is too reminiscent of Shakespeare's and vice-versa.

Let us record this bawdy species of figure congruence with a relational symbol '$\cong_{PUN}$'. It will thus denote the relation of identical puns holding within two distinct literary tracts, making for the following result.

GASCOIGNE: "Alas servant, what have I deserved that you come against me with naked **sword** as against an open enemy?"

$$\cong_{PUN}$$

SHAKESPEARE: Give us the **swords**, we have bucklers of our own.
Much Ado About Nothing, 5.2.

This kind of congruence constitutes a small part of the general pattern that characterizes Shakespeare and Gascoigne as one and the same author. To further illustrate this strain of overlap, recall the use of the item *prick* in the poem cited at the outset and consider in its wake the following example drawn from Shakespeare's *Love's Labor's Lost*.

> *Boyet.* A **mark**! O, mark but that **mark**! "A **mark**," says my lady!
> **Let the mark have a prick in't**, to mete at, if it may be.
> *Mar.* Wide o' the bow-hand! I' faith, your hand is out.
> *Cost.* Indeed 'a must shoot nearer, or he'll ne'er hit the clout.
> *Boyet.* An' if my hand be out, then belike your hand is in.
> *Love's Labour's Lost, 4.1.*

It should be clear that ***mark*** is a play on the female pudendum. By looking farther, it also becomes clear that the word ***pin*** participates alongside ***prick*** to playfully point to the same species of bawdy patter.

> *Cost.* Then will she get the upshot by cleaving the **pin**.
> *Mar.* Come, come, you talk greasily; your lips grow foul.
> *Cost.* She's too hard for you at **pricks**, sir. Challenge her to bowl.
> *Love's Labor's Lost, 4.1.*

With these, we have another example of punning congruence.

GASCOIGNE: *A brood of buds, well sharpèd in the* ***prick****:*

$$\cong_{PUN}$$

SHAKESPEARE: Let the mark have a **prick** in't,

Returning to Shakespeare's pun on *will* in *Sonnet 135,* we should not overlook that it is shared by Gascoigne, a fact that becomes obvious when we compare the latter with Shakespeare's first quatrain.

GASCOIGNE: *My loving love shall always work thy **will**.*
*It was thy **will** even thus to try my truth,*
*Thou hast thy **will**, my truth may now be seen,*
*It was thy **will that I** should <u>die in youth</u>,*
***Thou hast thy will**, my years are yet but green.*
Flowers.

139

$\cong_{PUN}$, $\cong_{LEX-9}$

SHAKESPEARE:

*Who ever hath her wish, **thou hast thy Will,***
*And **Will** to boot, and **will** in over-plus,*
*More than enough am **I that** vex thee still,*
*To thy sweet **will** making addition thus,*
Sonnet 135, 1-4.

One might question whether a penile pun is involved in the Gascoigne extract, but it does seem that one is intended in view of the potential pun on orgasm via the petite mort, *die in youth*. Whether or not one gets the bawdy reference, the lexical congruence with *will* mentioned in almost every line of both examples is sufficient to lend credibility to the claim that the two passages are the work of one and the same creator. Particularly obvious is the connection between the third line of the *Flowers* citation and the first line of *Sonnet 135*.

*Sonnet 135: Who ever hath her wish, **thou hast thy Will,***

$\cong_{LEX}$, $\cong_{SYN}$

Flowers: ***Thou hast thy will** my years are yet but green.*

Let us now recall Shakespeare's focus on *pins*. We have a good contender here for an analogue in *Freeman*, namely in *pens*. Gascoigne's choice of spelling discloses an intended penile pun.

And in very deed, it fell out that the Secretary having been
of long time absent and thereby **his** quills and **pēnes not worn**
so near as they were wont to be, **did now prick** such fair large
notes that his mistress liked better to sing faburden under him
than to descant any longer upon F.J.'s plain song.
Freeman, 88.

Of course orthography had not been standardized by Elizabethan times, so *pens* could be, and often was, spelled as *pennes*. A vowel with an overbar rendered as '$\bar{e}$' was not uncommonly employed by printers as a linear space-saving abbreviation of the sequence *en* or *em*. In particular, *pennes* could be written as *pēnes*. For a mind such as Oxford's, this orthographic option had the added effect of evoking an association with the word *penis*. That such a pun was indeed

140

intended in the above-cited example is clear from the passage as a whole, including the presence of the added pointed item, namely *prick*. Still another example is the following.

This manling, this minion, this slave, this secretary, was now by occasion ridden to London forsooth, and though his absence were unto her a disfurnishing of eloquence, it was yet unto F.J. an opportunity of good advantage, for when he perceived the change of her style and thereby grew in some suspicion that the same proceeded by absence of her chief chancellor, he thought good now to smite while the iron was hot and to lend his mistress such a **pen** in her secretary's absence as he should never be able at his return to amend the well writing thereof, wherefore according to her command he repaired once every day to her chamber at the least, whereas he guided himself so well and could devise such store of sundry pleasure and pastimes that he grew in favor not only with his desired, but also with the rest of the gentlewomen.
Freeman, 20.

The point, then, is that Gascoigne's pun on the stem *pens* is formally analogous to Shakespeare's pun on *pins*.

Pins, and poking-sticks of steel:
What maids lack from head to heel.
The Winter's Tale, 4.4.

Once the pun on *pens* is discerned, we may go on to recognize an analogous pun in the following passage drawn from *Freeman*.

I have thus far lamented that our countrymen have chosen rather to win a passover praise by **the wanton penning** of a few loving **lays** than to gain immortal fame by the clerkly handling of so profitable a theme.
Freeman, 4.

In this passage extracted from G.T.'s opening letter to his very friend, *penning* has the secondary reading of 'utilizing the penis', discernible once the sexual reading is conferred on the plausible quibble with the noun *lays*.

To summarize, a revealing similarity is evident between Shakespeare's handling of the penis and Gascoigne's. Such convergence involves at least the following vocabulary items, all illustrating the bawdy point of the associated wordplay.

SHAKESPEARE'S PUNS	GASCOIGNE'S PUNS
sword	*sword*
prick	*prick*
will	*will*
pins	*pēnes*

Speaking of pricks, let us briefly return to the couplet involving the nightingale reprinted on our page 109 of the novel.

The pretty bird that sings with prick against her breast,
Doth make a virtue of her need to watch when others rest.

That the word *prick* is intended to have a bawdy interpretation is clarified by a poem attributed to Thomas Lodge, entitled *Scillaes Metamorphosis.*

Under a poplar Themis did repose her,
And from a briar a sweetful branch did pluck.
When midst the briar ere she could scarce suppose her,
A nightingale 'gan sing, but woe the luck;
    The branch so near her breast, while she did quick her
    To tune her head, on sudden 'gan to prick her.

Whilst smiling Chlore midst her envious blushes,
Gan blame her fear and prettily said thus;
Worse pricks than these are found among these bushes,
And yet such pricks are scarcely feared of us.
    Nay soft, said Chelis, pricks do make birds sing,
    But pricks in ladies' bosoms often sting.

The word *sting*, it should be added, was often used as a pun on coitus, and of course *birds* was employed to denote *women,* as it is in England to this day. Shakespeare also evinces play on the *thorn* in *The Rape of Lucrece* but what is truly remarkable is his bawdy *burden-descant* play analogous to that noted above, cf. our page 92.

Moving from the male member to the female, we recall Shakespeare's bawdy *will*-sonnet whose first two quatrain we cited above. Now the third quatrain evinces still more cunning ingenuity.

> **The sea, all** *water, yet receive rain still,*
> *And in abundance addeth to his store,*
> *So thou being rich in Will add to thy Will,*
> *One will of mine to make thy large Will more.*
> *Sonnet 135, 9-12.*

Again the poet plays on his and his mistress' wills, four times in fact, while he exploits the sea as a metaphor for the vagina and rain, for semen. Do we encounter something similar in the novel?

> *Whereto I thus replied,*
> *Each fisherman can wish,*
> *That **all the sea** at every tide,*
> *Were his alone to fish.*

Apart from the added lexical item *all,* we have similar wordplay, provided we take *fish* to be a pun on *fuck*. Note further that the novelist's use of *seas* elsewhere in the novel might be provided what amounts to a Freudian interpretation.

> And by this means percase he [suspicion] had crept
> into the bosom of F.J. who, as is before declared, did
> erst swim in the **deepest seas of earthly delights**.

To summarize, the striking similarity of Shakespeare's bawdy wordplay with Gascoigne's, including a remarkable convergence of particular wordplay items and metaphors, provides us with another cogent indication that we are truly dealing with one and the same artistically wanton mind.

2.2 Ver-Play and El-Play

Changing courses briefly, we recall the following passage from *Hamlet*.

Horatio.	Hail to your lordship!
Hamlet.	I am glad to see you well. Horatio—or I do forget myself.

Horatio. The same, my lord, and your poor servant **ever**.
Hamlet.   Sir, my good friend—**I'll change that name**
            with you.
                    Hamlet, 1.2, 160-3.

The puzzle arising here is familiar to those who advance the Earl of Oxford as the genius lurking behind the *Shakespeare* pseudonym. The problem for all is to determine what name it is that Hamlet wishes to change with Horatio. Some orthodox editors gloss over the problem by alleging a figurative meaning, while others do not so much as recognize that a problem exists. For the sensitive reader who favors explanations over descriptions, it will be obvious that Hamlet wants to change, or perhaps exchange, the name *ever* with Horatio. This, however, makes no literal sense within the orthodox framework. It is no wonder that some orthodox scholars circumvent the problem by failing to note its existence.

It is crystal clear that the man behind the *Shakespeare* pseudonym is playing on his **name** by drawing on the word *ever* and this realization provides us with the punning inference *ever* = *E. Vere*. That this conclusion is on target is confirmed by allied data, not the least of which is that Hamlet's friends Horatio and Francisco are mirrored in real-life by de Vere's cousins Horace Vere and Frances Vere, the 'fighting Veres' of the war in the lowlands. That Horace was known as Horatio provides an additional item of confirmation. More considerations will be found in *Shakespeare's Fingerprints* and its sequels, or for that matter in just about any Oxfordian book or publication.

Now recall that Queen Elizabeth was likened to the phoenix, eternal and ever the same. This likeness relates to her motto *Semper Eadem*, which may be translated 'always the same'. We witness the conjunction of the phoenix and the motto in publishers' devices placed on the title pages of sixteenth century publications, the one pictured on the following page being a case in point, or closer to home, i.e. the royal home, the Tudor coat of arms replete with motto depicted in the second illustration.

An alternative translation of *Semper Eadem* is 'ever the same', the one in fact adopted by the orthodox scholar Leslie Hotson. It is this choice that would naturally be favored by de Vere, inasmuch as his favorite wordplay item *ever* makes an appearance in it by translation from the Latin. With these simple but cogent observations in

As it was plaid before the Queenes Maieftie,

Publisher's device illustrating the Queen's phoenix motto *Semper Eadem* appropriately complemented by the bird itself. The identical motto accompanies the Tudor coat of arms below.

mind, we are in a position to better comprehend the significance of the second quatrain of Shakespeare's *Sonnet 76.*

> *Why write I still all one, **ever the same**,*
> *And keep invention in a noted weed,*
> *That **every word doth almost tell my name**,*
> *Showing their birth and where they did proceed?*
> *Sonnet 76, 5-8.*

Within the orthodox framework of William of Stratford, this quatrain makes no good sense, since every word does not almost tell Shakespeare's name. If Shakespeare's name is *E. Vere,* however, the *every* word does indeed almost tell his name. The convergence of the word *every* with E. Vere as *name* in this case is thus quite analogous to the convergence of the word *ever* with E. Vere as *name* in the context of *Hamlet.*

An instance of *ever* is also encountered in the first line of the sonnet, which may be an additional play on the author E. Vere, but the more remarkable fact is that he is in some sense writing of the person identified with *ever the same,* who can be none other than Queen Elizabeth, as suggested by convergence with the motto *Semper Eadem.*

Some skeptics will suggest that the relation between the phrase *ever the same* and the motto *Semper Eadem* is sheer coincidence. That such an allegation is itself contrived is shown by a Latin poem noted by Yates [1975] to which we have added boldface type font.

> **Una** quod es **semper**, quod semper es optima princeps,
>   Quam bene convenient hae duo verba tibi:
> Quod ia, quod prudens, quod casta, quod innuba Viorgo
>   Semper es, hoc etiam *Semper* **es** *Una* modo.
> Et Populum quod ames, Populo quod amata vicissim
>   Semper es, hic constans *Semper* et *Una* manes.
> O utinam quoniam sic *semper* es, *una* liceret,
>   **Una** te nobis **semper**, **Eliza**, frui.

One need not understand Latin to comprehend that these lines, written on the occasion of the Queen's visit to Audley End in 1578, address Queen Eliza herself. Now the juxtaposition of *Una* and *Semper* throughout makes clear that Elizabeth is to be viewed as

Una, the unique empress, i.e. the One, as recognized by the orthodox Yates. It follows that whenever we encounter a juxtaposition of *una* with *semper,* whether in Latin or in English translation, we should consider whether the poetry is not touching on the Queen in some way or other. But this is precisely what we encounter in *Sonnet 76* whose relevant line is *Why write I still all* **one, ever the same.**

The presence of **one** and **ever the same** provides an argument that Shakespeare was writing about or to Queen Elizabeth, and one must seriously doubt that a commoner from Stratford would have had the prerogative of doing so.

One may also conjecture that the word *weed,* meaning 'guise' or 'garment' and hence not unreasonably in this context 'disguise', adds to the veracity of our claim that this quatrain involves a hidden message. Nor is it difficult to see that the word *birth* suggests high birth, though we suspect that orthodox apologists will find it hard to swallow the possibility, much less digest it.

Reasonable minds will conclude that certain puzzles in Shakespeare's plays and poetry begin to come into focus, thereby making good sense, once we identify their hidden author as E. Vere. The very convergence of the *name*-puzzles, one in *Hamlet* and one in *Sonnet 76* would seem to confirm our previous conclusions.

From here we may turn to what at first blush appears to be a harder nut to crack, a comment made by Mercutio in *Romeo and Juliet,* with the understanding that the word *cheverell,* with modern rendition *cheveril,* is kid leather, which easily stretches, especially when wet.

> O! Here is a wit of **cheverell**, that stretches from an inch
> narrow to an ell broad.
> *Romeo and Juliet 2.4.*

How are we to understand this remark over and beyond Mercutio's intended praise for Romeo's wit? In particular, why does Shakespeare pick on the word **cheverell**? And what is the significance of the *inch* and the *ell*? Orthodox editors of *Romeo and Juliet* fail to enlighten us. Indeed, we will find that by emending Shakespeare's *cheverell* to modern *cheveril,* they effectively destroy Shakespeare's intended identification of the terminal segment of *cheverell* with that of an ell broad.

147

A first approximation at understanding Mercutio's remark can be gleaned by turning to Holland's book of 1923.

> 'Cheveril' in the original is spelt "cheverell," and inch is either "inche" or "ynche." It will be noticed, therefore, that the word "cheverell" ends with "ell" and it commences with "che." "Che" is three-fifths of the word "inche" and is therefore "an inche narrow." Now let us stretch the word cheverell a little. Thus:
>
> Che – ver – ell
>
> We find the word "ver" stretching from the inch narrow to ell broad. Vere, or Ver, is the Earl of Oxford's own name, and thus no doubt is left as to whom the wit of cheverell stretching from an inch narrow to an ell broad refers.
>
> Holland [1923: 72]

The *cheverell* riddle provides us with another instance of the author's *ver*-play at its best, for here he clearly identifies himself with Romeo. What Holland did not point out, however, is that Mercutio's remark includes an unmistakably bawdy reading, with **ell broad** a subtle reference to Romeo's first love Rosaline. We see this when we recall that Mercutio is speaking of Romeo vis-à-vis Rosaline and by noting that the word *wit* was used as a pun on the male member and that an ell is a measure of forty-five inches, which is broad indeed for the thing of bawdy reference in this case.

It is now clear that Romeo's wit extends in such a way as to be consistent with the stretchability of kidskin leather. Moreover, it stretches toward his mistress, who is that same dark lady whose wit is as broad as her will is large and spacious, as revealed in the *Will*-sonnet cited in the last section. By Holland's discovery, we see that the Oxford earl himself, namely Vere, is one whose wit stretches toward his mistress's ell. And who might Mistress Ell be? In light of *Sonnet 76,* we should certainly investigate the possibility that she is the Queen. That view, moreover, is supported by its convergence with the *ell* sequence of the word *cheverell*. Finally, the two points mesh with the name Rosaline, as *Rosa* is a plausible allusion to the Tudor rose.

Since de Vere may be telling us that his wit stretches in the presence of the Queen, we are led to ask whether there is any documentary evidence to bear out the suggested interpretation, confirming that we are not just stretching a point for the reader's entertainment pleasure. A suggestion of love matters can indeed be found by a deeper sounding of the letter from Gilbert Talbot.

> My Lord of Oxford is lately grown into great credit, for the Queen's Majesty delighteth more in his personage and his dancing and his valiantness than any other. I think Sussex doth back him all that he can. If it were not for his fickle head he would pass any of them shortly. My Lady Burghley unwisely hath declared herself, as it were, jealous, which is come to the Queen's ear: whereat she hath been not a little offended with her, but now she is reconciled again. At all these **love matters** my Lord Treasurer [= Lord Burghley] winketh, and will not meddle in any way.
> *Gilbert Talbot to the Earl of Shrewsbury, 11 May 1573.*

The interpretation of *love matters* may well differ from critic to critic, but what is plausible based on these citations is that our genius makes bawdy references in connection with the Queen.

For yet another convincing example of *ver*-play, consider *Sonnet 105* in which de Vere cleverly signs off on every quatrain.

> *Let not my love be called idolatry,*
> *Nor my belovèd as an idol show,*
> *Since all alike my songs and praises be*
> *To one, of one, still such, and **ever so**.*

> *Kind is my love today, tomorrow kind,*
> *Still constant in a wondrous excellence;*
> *Therefore my verse to constancy confined,*
> *One thing expressing, leaves out **difference**.*

> *Fair, kind, and true, is all my argument,*
> *Fair, kind, and true, varying to other words;*
> *And in this change is my invention spent,*
> *Three themes in one, which wondrous scope **affords**.*

The fact that three instances of wordplay appear in the terminus of all three quatrains, each one identifying Vere by a pun on his family name or title, is no accident.

149

ever so	*e-ver so*
difference	*di-ffere-nce*
affords	*Ox-ford*

The fact that Shakespeare plays on his Oxford title by drawing on the words like *ford* is argued in some detail in *Shakespeare's Fingerprints* and one may also consider that *so* in the phrase *ever so* is a play on the Seventeenth **O**xford.

Nor is it difficult to recognize additional items of wordplay in the three quatrains. We have already met with the word *fair*, which is a potential play on the author's family name *Vere*, whereas the word **true** relates to *Vere* via the family motto *Vero Nihil Verius,* 'nothing truer than a Vere = truth'. In other words, truth is itself a *ver*-word by translation into Latin, what we might call a *ver*-translate. The astute reader will not fail to also note the phrase *varying to other words,* with **varying** serving as one more clever example of *ver*-play. From this preponderance of wordplay items, we conclude that *kind* also relates to Vere, although what is involved here is less clear. The word is cognate with *kin* and Shakespeare himself relates *kind* and *kin* in *Hamlet,* so we may conjecture that *kind* too relates to the family Vere.

With these preliminaries considered, we may return to the initial quatrain, noting Shakespeare's continuing obsession with the **one** and comparing it with the related line from *Sonnet 76.*

SONNET 105:   *To **one**, of **one**, still such, and **ever** so.*
SONNET 76:   *Why write I still all **one**, **ever** the same,*

Relatedness of the two lines is quickly perceived. The focus on *one* in *of one* is again a plausible reference to the Queen. This analysis in turn lends credence to a regal interpretation of the climax of *Sonnet 105.*

> *Fair, kind, and true, have often lived **alone**,*
> *Which three till now **never kept seat in one**.*

As we will eventually see, **alone** is analogous to **all one**, the phrase we encountered in *Sonnet 76.* Now **never** is a plausible pun on Ned Vere, the name *Ned* being a well-documented variant of the first name *Edward,* Oxford's first name. If **one** denotes Queen Elizabeth, as suggested by reference to her as **Una**, we have another potentially bawdy item of wordplay.

2.3. Will I Am

The name *George Gascoigne* was associated with a number of works, including a commendatory poem in a translation of a book written by Cardano. The dedicatory letter of the translation is dated 1571 and the work bears the title *Cardanus Comforte*. It includes a letter signed by de Vere along with a poem bearing his signature. A poem bearing the signature George Gascoigne also appears in the front matter of the translation, but it is a later work associated with the name *Gascoigne* that we wish to draw on to augment our claim that the name is to be identified as a pseudonym for Edward de Vere. In particular, in *Hemetes the Heremyte* we encounter a mysterious illustration accompanied by a revealing poem. The poem is to be interpreted in light of our earlier discussion and commences in the following way.

*Behold, good Queen, a poet with a **spear**,*
*Strange sights **well marked** are understood the better,*
*A soldier armed, with **pencil in his hair**,*
*With **pen to fight** and **sword to write a letter**,*

His gown half off, his blade not fully bound
In doubtful dumps, which way were best to take
With humble heart and knees that kiss the ground
Presents himself to you for duty's sake

Literally these lines correspond to the picture provided on the following page; our boldfacing is for facility of reference. The sonnet continues:

And thus he saith, no danger, I protest,
*Shall **ever** let this loyal heart I bear*
To serve you so as may become me best
In field, in town, in court, or anywhere.

151

Finally, the terminal couplet:

*Then peerless prince, employ this **willing man***
*In your **affairs** to do the best he can.*
    Tam Marti quam Mercurio

The illustration and poem provide a wealth of material that cries out for elucidation. The poem is usually interpreted as a request by the real-life George Gascoigne for preferment or patronage from Queen Elizabeth. We claim that it is a supplication by the Earl of Oxford and that it includes a spate of sexual innuendos, many of which we are now in a position to comprehend. Among these are quibbles related to the well-pointed objects **spear**, **pencil**, **pen**, and **blade**, all intimately related to a **well-marked**

sight and gown half off as complements to the blade not fully bound, which we may take to be related to the pencil in the author's hair (which hair?) and the pen with which to fight in the manner of *militia amoris*. Perhaps the battle is to extend even so far as her aft airs, as a bawdy interpretation of **affairs** suggests.

The poet was truly a **willing man** in the literal sense of desiring to serve the Queen and protect her realm. Such willingness, however, also included action consonant with his bawdy wordplay. Such wordplay is unexpected and hardly likely from the soldier George Gascoigne, which accounts for why orthodox scholars are unable to detect it, since they do believe that the poem was penned by a soldier. In striking contrast, it is expected of Edward de Vere and is consistent with his status as courtier and former favorite of the Queen, but also as the cleverly bawdy poet-playwright behind the *Shakespeare* pseudonym. Indeed, the bawdy interpretation we have advanced is consonant with that of *Sonnet 151,* widely recognized for its bawdy content.

> But rising at thy name doth point out thee,
> As his triumphant prize—proud of this pride,
> He is contented thy poor drudge to be,
> To **stand in thy affairs**, fall by thy side.
>
> No want of conscience hold it that I call
> Her love for whose dear love **I rise and fall**.

The Gascoigne poem is a reflection of the archetypal Mars-Mercury aspect of the poet, consonant with the *Tam Marti quam Mercurio* motto that punctuates the poem and hangs from the hole in the ceiling in the picture, held by a hand extending through it.

Supplication to Queen Elizabeth is reflected in the illustration, which includes a number of potential references to Oxford, apart from the spear itself. To understand the more subtle allusions, it is necessary to recall that de Vere played incessantly on his Oxford title, as we have witnessed in connection with several examples cited above. To mention another example, the name *Ophelia* can be segmented as *O-phel-ia* and thus interpreted as the 'lover of O', compliant with the obvious parse of the name into its minimally significant parts. Our approach accounts for de Vere's choice of many such names, including *Othello*, the tragic protagonist modeled on Oxford himself and the name *Oberon,* Lord of the **Fair**ies, and still other names of characters, some utilized as pseudonyms, many of which are explored in *Shakespeare's Fingerprints*. Finally, it accounts for Shakespeare's deployment of vocative *O* in a variety of contexts, as well as play involving little *o,* as in the following lines from *Romeo and Juliet.*

Benvolio.   Here comes Romeo, here comes Romeo.
Mercutio.   Without his roe, like a dried herring

The last line inspires various readings, including the bawdy one appropriate to Romeo's return from a night under the balcony of one who Mercutio thinks is Rosaline, for which roe, 'eggs', are interpreted as Romeo's testicles. More engaging, Shakespeare invites us to remove the sequence *Ro* from the name *Romeo,* whereupon we are left with *meo,* or more transparently, *me o,* and clearer still, *me O(xford),* as Romeo was truly modeled on the Oxford Vere, consistent with the earlier play on *cheverell.*

The levitating laureate's garland in the above illustration represents one more aspect of de Vere's ox-play with another potential relationship to big *O,* as perhaps also does the circular hole in the ceiling. Such circular objects may also be bawdily symbolic, consistent with those examples framed in Chapter 0 of *Shakespeare's Fingerprints.* As for the spear that Oxford-Gascoigne bears in the above picture, it too relates to his bawdy play on swords and other pointed objects whose theme we have elaborated above.

The spear's formal reflection in the name *Shakespeare* is perhaps one more play in the same spirit, indicating to readers or auditors that the author is he who shakes his spear in light-hearted jest. This interpretation is further suggested by an analysis of the first name *William,* in which we may capitalize the second *i* as an aid to comprehending the comedian's hidden humor.

Will-I-am

The name *William Shakespeare* is thus an excellent candidate for a bawdonym, our designation for those pseudonyms adopted by Oxford to showcase bawdy punning potential, a number of which items fit into his rich wordplay arsenal. Such revelation, however, was intended only for those bright enough to perceive it, which pretty much excludes orthodox professors in our own day.

A potential bawdonym is also the name *George Gascoigne* with emphasis on gas, as is the name *George Whetstone,* also written by our prankster as *Whetstones,* with a possible play on both *wet* and *stones,* the latter an Elizabethan term for testicles.

3. CHARACTERS AND MODELS

We have noted that some orthodox scholars have sensed that the Freeman Jones novel is a *roman à clef,* a point of view explaining why *Flowers* was revised, with its setting moved from England to Italy. This take on the novel also explains, at least in part, why de Vere appropriated the name of real-life Elizabethan soldier and Secret Service agent George Gascoigne, as the pseudonym is found in certain poems in *Flowers* and on the very title page of the expurgated revision.

The change of the name *Freeman Jones* of the original book to *Ferdinando* in the revision supports the claim that the character F. J. was modeled on the author himself since the initial sequence *Ferdi* is an obvious play on the family name: *Ferdi ← di Fer = de Vere.* Hence the name *Freeman Jones* is itself a permutation *fer*-word of the type abundantly adduced in *Shakespeare's Fingerprints.* Thus, the first name *Freeman* is a likely permutation by dint of the orthographic transformation *Fere → Free,* thereby enfolding shades of the Vere man. One finds empirical support for our conjecture that Freeman Jones or F.J. is modeled on de Vere in the domain of margination, a topic discussed below in the Appendix and in more detail in *Never and For Ever.* In particular, we find a clue on page 242 of the original publication, reproduced on our next page.

By invoking margination, the author plays on his name *E. Vere,* and what is more, by following that identification with the initials *F.I.,* he effectively signals that the protagonist is to be identified with the living author E.Vere.

That de Vere identifies with his male protagonist is consistent with his shadowing of himself in the dramatis personae Hamlet, Romeo, Othello, Benedick, Berowne, and other Shakespearean protagonists. That his prose would also include characters modeled on real-life personages is consistent with these dramatic examples and many others.

242 The aduentures

that the same is the moze apte meane of introdudion to ƀ
verses, which J meane to reherse vnto you, and J think
you wil not disdaine to read my conceipt with his inuen‐
tion about declaration of his commedie. The next that e‐
uer F.I. wzote the,vpon any aduſture hapned betwene
him and this fayze Lady, was this as J haue heard him
say, and vppon this occasion. After he grew moze bold &
better acquaynted with his Miſtreſſe diſpoſition, he ad‐
uentured one Fryday in the mozning to go vnto hir chã‐
ber,and theruppon wzote as followeth: which he termed
a Frydayes Bzeakefaſt.   *G.T.*

T *That selfe same day, and of that day that hower,*
  When she doth raigne, that mockt Vulcane the Smith:
And thought it meete to harbor in hir bower,
Some gallant geſt for hir to dally with.
That bleſſed hower, that bliſt and happie daye,
I thought it meete, with haſtie ſteppes to go:
Vnto the lodge, wherein my Lady laye,
To laugh for ioye, or ells to weepe for wo.
And lo, my Lady of hir wonted grace,
Firſt lent hir lippes to me(as for a kiſſe:)
And after that hir body to embrace,
Wherein dame nature wrought nothing amiſſe.
What followed next, geſſe you that knowe the trade,
For in this sort, my Frydayes feaſt I made.
     F. I.

T His Sonet is ſhozt and ſwéete, reaſonably well, ac‐
cozding to the occaſion &c. Many dayes paſſed theſe
two louers with great delight , their affayzes being no
leſſe polltikely gouerned, than happely atchiued. And
ſurely J haue heard F. I. affirme in ſad earneſt, that hee
did not onely loue hir, but was furthermoze ſo ratiſyed
in Extaſies with continual remembzance of his delights,
                          that

To aid the reader in grasping the point about character figuration, we briefly turn to another work, a collection of short stories entitled *A Petite Pallace of Pettie His Pleasure* attributed to George Pettie. In this collection published in 1576 we find introductory letters having much in common with the *Freeman* novel, as a comparison will readily reveal.

FREEMAN: H. **VV.** to the Reader.

In August last-passed, **my** familiar **friend** Master G.T. bestowed upon me the reading of a written book, wherein he had collected divers **discourses** and verses, invented upon sundry **occasions** by sundry gentlemen, in mine opinion right commendable for their capacity. And here withal **my said friend charged me that I should use them only for mine own particular commodity** and eftsoons safely deliver the original copy to him again, wherein I must confess myself but half a merchant, **for the copy** unto him I have safely redelivered. But the work—for I thought it worthy to be **published**—I have entreated my friend A.B. to **imprint**: as one that thought **better to please a number by common commodity than to feed the humor of any private person** by needless singularity.

$\cong$*LEX-28*, $\cong$*ESTRANGE*

PETITE PALLACE:

TO THE GENTLE
GENTLEWOMEN READERS

Gentle readers, whom by my will I would have only gentlewomen, and therefore to you I direct my words. May it please you to understand, that the great desire I have to procure your delight hath caused me somewhat to transgress the bounds of faithful friendship: **for** having with great earnestness obtained of **my** very **friend** Master George Pettie **the copy** of certain histories by himself, upon his own and certain of his friends' private **occasions** drawn into **discourses**, I saw such witty and pithy pleasantness contained in them, that I thought I could not any way do greater pleasure or better service to your noble sex, than to publish them in print, to your common profit and pleasure. And though I am sure hereby to incur his displeasure, for that **he willed me in any wise to keep them**

secret, yet if it please you thankfully to accept my good will, I force the less of his ill will. For to speak my fancy without feigning, **I care not to displease twenty men to please one woman**; for the friendship amongst men is to be counted but cold kindness, in respect of the fervent affections between men and women: and our nature is rather to dote of women, than to love men.

Apart from the impressive lexical overlap that they exhibit, the two letters agree in the four respects listed below for facility of reference.

i. Both are alleged to be by a friend of the author.
ii. The author does not want his work to be published. (Indeed he has not granted permission for the friend to show the material elsewhere.)
iii. The friend goes against the author's desire, responding in the same way: Gascoigne's friend H.W. and Pettie's friend R.B. both secure publication of the respective author's work.
iv. Publication is secured for similar reasons, i.e. to please others: "to please a number by common commodity" in one case and "to please" women in the other.

All of the above relate to the literary method of estrangement, a device whereby the author distances himself or herself from the text so as to render it more "real". The device becomes prominent with the rise of realism, but as we so often find, Shakespeare was far a-head of his time. Adopting the relational symbol '$\cong_{ESTRANGE}$', we have signaled between the two extracts that both are related by virtue of including this method of estrangement. This squares with the claim provided in our footnote on page 5 to the effect that H.W. is to be identified with G.T. and F.J., and ultimately Oxford.

Now points (*i*)-(*iv*) are precisely those found in a letter signed by Oxford and published as a commendatory introduction to *Cardanus Comforte,* a translation of the Italian mathematician-philosopher-physician Cardano's book of consolation, allegedly carried out by Thomas Bedingfeld by commandment of the Earl of Oxford. In this remarkable letter Oxford broaches the issue of whether or not to publish the book and in so doing he confirms all four of the above points. Thus, he confirms point (*i*) to the effect that the alleged translator Bedingfeld is a dear friend.

After I had perused your letters, good Master Bedingfeld, finding in them your request far differing from the desert of your labor, I could not chose but greatly doubt whether it were better for me to yield you your desire or excuse mine own intention towards the publishing of your book. For I do confess the affections that I have always born towards you could move me not a little.

Indeed, the very title of the letter confirms the friendship, as it begins: "To my louinge frend Thomas *Bedingfeld Esquyer.*" Next Oxford makes crystal clear that the friend desires that the work not be published and that he, Oxford, is going against his friend's wishes, thereby confirming points (*ii*) and (*iii*).

But when I had th[o]roughly considered in my mind of sundry and divers arguments whether it were best to obey mine affections or the merits of your studies, at the length I determined it better to deny your unlawful request than to grant or condescend to the concealment of so worthy a work.

Oxford also confirms point (*iv*), exactly as he does covertly in *Flowers* and in the work ascribed to Pettie. "Whereby as you have been profited in the translating, so many may reap knowledge by the reading of the same ..." Indeed, later in the letter, we find a passage offering a stunning convergence with both *Flowers* and the Pettie book.

OXFORD TO BEDINGFELD:
... and **better I thought** it were to **displease one**, than **to displease** many...

FREEMAN: H. VV. to the Reader.
I have entreated my friend A.B. to imprint: as **one** that **thought better to please** a number by common commodity **than to** feed the humor of any private person ...

PETITE PALLACE:
For to speak my fancy without feigning, **I** care not **to displease** twenty men **to please one** woman;

In view of the subtle similarities that we have witnessed in the cited passages, one would be foolish to redescribe the observed relations by alleging pilfering or plagiarism. Nor can we excuse the estrangement as mere commonplace, for that would fail to explain the impressive overlap with respect to wording. The only account yielding explanatory value posits a single bright creator employing the same literary device of estrangement in all three works. With one creator, it is expected that similar phrasing should emerge. In view of the commendatory letter in *Cardanus,* moreover, bearing the Earl of Oxford's signature as *E. Oxenford,* that mind, we must conclude, was Oxford's, and we are led to conjecture that Cardano's book was translated by Oxford himself, with the name *Thomas Bedingfeld* serving as an additional pseudonym.

Restricting to *Freeman* and the *Petite Pallace,* we find further confirmation of our claims when we consider additional introductory letters. For starters, the associated headings of two letters are revealingly similar.

FREEMAN: **The letter of G.T. to** *his very friend* **H.W. concerning this work.**

PETITE PALLACE: **The letter of G.P. to R.B. concerning this work.**

Pursuing the point about going against the alleged author's will, when we pass to a comparison of extracts from these two letters we discover new points of contact supporting our thesis.

PETITE PALLACE:
> Forced by your earnest importunity, and furthered by mine own idle **opportunity, I** have set down in writing, and according to **your** request sent unto you, certain of those tragical trifles, which you have heard me in sundry companies at sundry times report, and so near as I could I have written them word for word as I then told them; … but whether they seem unto you good or ill, I trust **you will take** them as a token of **good will**, and that is the only commodity I look to reap by them. I pray you only to use them to your own private pleasure, and not to impart them to other, perchance to my prejudice, for that **divers** discourses touch nearly divers of my near friends;

but … **only** they whom they touch, can understand whom they touch; yet to avoid all captious constructions, <u>I pray you in any wise let them be an object **only** for **your own** eyes.</u>

FLOWERS:

Remembering the late conference passed between us in my lodging and how you seemed to esteem some pamphlets which I did there show unto you far above their worth in skill, **I** did straightway conclude the same <u>**your** judgment</u> to proceed of two especial causes, one—and principal—the steadfast **good will** which you have ever hitherto, sithens our first familiarity, borne towards me … I **only** do adventure thus to participate the sight thereof unto your former good will, even so <u>that you will by no means make the same common, but after **your own** recreation</u> **taken** therein that **you will** safely redeliver unto me the original copy. For otherwise I shall not only provoke all the authors to be offended with me, but farther shall lease the **opportunity** of a greater matter, half and more granted unto me already by the willing consent of one of them. …

Yours or not his own.
G. T.

In the first letter the author entreats his friend not to impart his writing to others, but rather to reserve it for himself. This is what is said in the second letter associated with the novel, albeit in different words, which we have again underscored for ease of reference along with boldface type font to signal lexical overlap. To emphasize this result, we record the observed convergence with a formal statement.

PETTIE-FREEMAN ENTREATY: *In both works the author entreats his friends not to impart his work to others, but to reserve it for himself.*

Once again the striking fact is that this is precisely what we find in the introductory letter to *Cardanus Comforte,* the letter in this case attributed to Thomas Bedingfeld, with additional lexical overlap as indicated by our inclusion of boldface type font.

I do present the book your Lordship so long desired with assured hope that howsoever you mislike or allow thereof, <u>you will favorably conceal mine imperfection which to</u>

your Lordship **alone** I dare discover ... My meaning was
not to have **imparted** my travail to any, **but your** honor
hath power to countermand mine intention. Yet **I** most
humbly beseech you either **not to make** any partakers
thereof, or at the least wise those, who for reverence to
your L. or love to me, will willingly bear with mine errors.

As we have noted with respect to points (*i*)-(*iv*) above, the entreaty here is that found in the other two works, i.e. in the *Pettie-
Freeman Entreaty*. But this clearly demonstrates that a solitary clever genius stands behind all three works.

In the last-cited Pettie letter, the author admits that the stories
touch **divers** of his near friends (i.e. de Vere's friends), which is
tantamount to admitting that his characters are modeled on real-life
individuals. It is natural to expect the same to hold of the characters
in the Freeman Jones novel, all the more so in view of the fact that
Oxford utilized a similar introductory strategy in both works. Pursuing their identification and granting that Freeman Jones or F.J. is
modeled after Edward de Vere, we naturally ask about F.J.'s mistress Elinor. In view of the *el*-play discussed in section 2, one is certainly warranted to conjecture that Elinor is modeled on Queen Elizabeth.

Precisely this proposal has been advanced in an interesting book
by Dickinson [2002:173-88], while the proposition was conjectured
independently in *Shakespeare's Fingerprints*. When we recall that
Queen Elizabeth was likened to Diana, whose heavenly aspect is the
moon and who was often denoted by the name *Cynthia,* we have
excellent grounds for concluding that Oxford-Gascoigne was indeed
referring to Queen Elizabeth when he included the poem referring
to Cynthia and the moon in his novel, a poem repeated above in
section 1. Thus, the Queen is mentioned in the novel, whether or not
she is to be identified as the prototype of Elinor.

Like Ophelia—whose name we have elsewhere claimed signals
the lover of O, i.e. Oxford—Frances may be modeled on Burghley's
elder daughter Anne Cecil. Dickinson advances a not implausible
element of potential wordplay in support of this claim, conjecturing
that the name *Fraunces,* as it was originally spelled, is a play on
Frau Cecil. If this is correct, we should not modernize *Fraunces* as
Frances, while another possibility is that the name *Anne* is itself to
be visualized in *Fraunces.* In other words, since Anne Cecil was de

Vere's first wife, the following segmentation proves tenable.

Fr—aun—ces ≡ Vere Anne Cec(il)

Dickinson notes that the Earl of Leicester may very well qualify as Elinor's secretary, while noting also the possible candidacy of Sir Christopher Hatton. During the period the novel was written, Queen Elizabeth was close to Hatton, a man known to have been jealous of Oxford's relationship with the Queen. Surviving correspondence attests to the fact that Hatton functioned as her private secretary, much as the novel's pygmy functioned as Elinor's. Thus, Hatton must be considered a strong candidate for Elinor's secretary.

From the identification of Frances as Anne Cecil, it follows that the Lord or Knight of the Castle was drawn after William Cecil, Lord High Treasurer and we emerge with all of the following denotation relations pertaining to most of the novel's characters.

Frances ≡ Anne Cecil Vere
Knight of the Castle ≡ William Cecil, Lord Burghley
Freeman Jones ≡ Edward de Vere
Elinor ≡ Queen Elizabeth
Secretary ≡ Christopher Hatton or the Earl of Leicester

Some such identifications as these, along with the bawdy aspect of both the poetry and the novel, is presumably what forced Oxford to partially sanitize the original production as the one later published under the *Gascoigne* pseudonym. This need is clarified by the author's subsequent commentary on his poems, those being Oxford's, and not the real-life Gascoigne's.

> I find that some of them have not only been offensive
> for sundry wanton speeches and lascivious phrases,
> but further I hear that the same have been doubtfully
> construed, and (therefore) scandalous.
> Cunliffe [1907: 3]

Sir Christopher Hatton

ELINOR'S SECRETARY'S DESCRIPTION:

He was in height the proportion of two pygmies, in breadth the thickness of two bacon hogs, of presumption a giant, of power a gnat, apishly witted, knavishly mannered, and crabbedly savored.

Apparently the expurgated version did not achieve its intended goal, as it too was destined for censorship, a claim that the orthodox Prouty supports with the following evidence.

> That he was not successful in this bold device is indicated by an entry in the "B" Book of the Stationers' Company recording the seizure, by the authorities in 1576, of "half a hundred of Gascoignes poesies."
>
> Prouty [1942: 194]

Additional considerations appear to support Dickinson's identification of Elinor as Queen Elizabeth. One such item recalls a species of bawdy wordplay like that witnessed above in Section 2. To see this, note first a wittily racy passage from *Hamlet* concerning country matters.

Hamlet.	Lady, shall I lie in your lap?
	[Sits down at Ophelia's feet.]
Ophelia.	No, my lord.
Hamlet.	I mean, my head upon your lap?
Ophelia.	Ay, my lord.
Hamlet.	Do you think I meant **count**ry matters?
Ophelia.	I think nothing, my lord.
Hamlet.	That's a fair thought to lie **between maids' legs**.

The palpable play on *cunt* is showcased by our addition of boldface type font. The point is that in the Freeman Jones novel we encounter a related passage.

> Well, thus these two lovers passed many days in exceeding **cont**entation and more than speakable pleasures,

That the pleasures of which the author writes include those that are unspeakable suggests that the word *contentation* involves a play analogous to that of Hamlet's *country*. On the other hand, whereas Oxford-Shakespeare's *country* quibble refers to Ophelia, a shadow of Anne Cecil, his *contentation* play in the novel relates to Elinor, a possible figuration of Elizabeth, otherwise known as Gloriana. With this latter epithet in mind, we continue the last quote from the novel:

in which time F.J. did compile very many verses according to sundry occasions proffered, whereof I have not obtained the most at his hands and the reason that he deemed me the same was that—as he alleged—they were for the most part soured with a taste of **glory**.

And thus we exit with a plausible play on the name *Gloriana*, which would seem to provide strong support of Dickinson's claim. Once again, this manner of wordplay is found in Oxford's poetry as it appeared under the *Shakespeare* pseudonym.

> *Full many a **glorious** morning have I seen*
> *Flatter the mountain tops with **sovereign** eye,*
> *Kissing with golden face the meadows green,*
> *Gilding pale streams with heavenly alchemy;*
> *Sonnet 33, 1-4.*

Indeed, the sovereign eye is the eye of the sovereign as clarified by the presence of the word *glorious,* a plausible play on her well-known *Gloriana* epithet. This interpretation is consistent with what has been noted above in Section 2 and is further supported by the third quatrain of the same sonnet.

> *Even so **my sun** one early morn did shine,*
> *With all triumphant splendor on my brow;*
> *But out alack, he was but one hour mine,*
> *The **region** cloud hath masked him from me now.*
> *Sonnet 33, 9-12.*

The *region cloud* in this case is an intended play on the regent, who has masked the sun, i.e. the son, from his father, a point briefly discussed below. Additional passages from the novel can be viewed as confirming the identification of Elinor as Eliza, among which we will cite two snippets relating to the Queen's lunar aspect.

The occasion—as I have heard him rehearse—was by encounter that he had with his lady by light of the **moon**. And forasmuch as the moon in midst of their delights did vanish away, or was overspread with a cloud, thereupon he took the subject of his theme. And thus it ensueth, called 'A **Moon**shine Banquet'.

Although words like *encounter* may, in the spirit of the last example, be intended to have a bawdy reading, it is the focus on *his lady by the light of moon* that brings to the fore the lunar aspect, again related to the Queen in a wealth of poetic works written during the Elizabethan timeframe. Whereas the moonshine banquet transpires by the light of the moon, the next passage indicates that that light emanates from Elinor.

> Even so my friend F.J., lately overcome by the
> **beautiful beams of this dame Elinor** and having now
> committed his most secret intent to these late rehearsed
> letters, was at unwares encountered with his friendly foe
> and constrained either to prepare some new defense or else
> like a recreant to yield himself as already vanquished.

If Elinor is the source of moonbeams, then she *is* the moon, whence we have another plausible identification of her as Queen. Whether or not this identification is correct, it is clear that Cynthia is indeed the Queen as we recall her in the novelist's poem:

> *Yet honored still the Moon with true intent:*
> *Who taught us skill,*
> *To work our will,*
> *And gave us place till all the night was spent.*

The night was spent making love and it is the Moon who taught the author skill to work his will, with an associated bawdy play on the word *will,* noted in Section 2. In light of so much erotic play, one need only return to the first quatrain of *Sonnet 33* cited above on the previous page and note that the phrases *mountain tops* and *pale streams* also have their obvious bawdy readings.

The identification of Elinor with the Queen may seem to some readers a bold conjecture, but Elinor is in fact referred to as Queen on page 21 of our edition and *my Queen* is found in the poetry on page 48. Moreover, we find mention of Court on page 58, and when we return to Oxford's poetry and wordplay, we discern an obsession with the Queen that is strongly supportive of it. For example, is the following passage found on page 96 not a dead give-away?

The ladies at their return found **the court in Dame Elinor's chamber**, who had there assembled her secretary, Dame Pergo, and the rest.

Some Oxfordians have claimed the fair youth of Shakespeare's sonnets to be Oxford's son. Indeed, gleanings from the sonnets to that effect are laid out in some detail in Chapter 8 of *Shakespeare's Fingerprints*. Orthodoxy's favored candidate for the fair youth is Henry Wriothesley, 3rd Earl of Southampton. His motto is repeated below.

SOUTHAMPTON'S MOTTO: *Ung par tout,* ***tout par ung.***

This motto—*One for all, all for one*—may be crucial to a correct reading of the second quatrain of *Sonnet 76,* provided earlier. Indeed, it is the second conjunct of that motto that yields evidence of *all one* as related wordplay in the relevant line of the sonnet:

*Why write I still **all one** ever the same,*

We have confirmation that Shakespeare-Oxford was addressing his son and we emerge accordingly with the following revised list of wordplay items alongside the individuals to whom they allude.

all one : Southampton
one : Una = Queen Elizabeth
ever the same : Queen Elizabeth

Thus, *one* relates to both Southampton and the Queen and this finding now inspires us to return to the fourth line of *Sonnet 105.*

*To **one**, of **one**, still such, and **ever so**.*

Remarkably we find two occurrences of *one,* correlating with *all one* and *Una.* In other words, *Sonnet 105* is a song and praise addressed to Una's son by *ever,* just as *Sonnet 76* is a sonnet directed to a son with respect to *Semper Eadem,* and *Sonnet 33* a sonnet about a son as he relates to the sovereign. It is also plausible that *still such* is a variation on the *Semper Eadem* motto, so we have *one still such,* i.e. Una the Queen. In conclusion, two *one*'s and *ever* correlate with *fair, kind,* and *true* of the above-cited sonnet. Nor should it be missed that throughout the sixteenth century and earlier the word *kind* related to birth, hence high birth, and as a noun was related to royalty.

A consequence of this analysis is that it has explanatory value. To cite but one consequence, it reveals the deeper significance of the fair youth's bastard signs included in *Sonnet 68*.

> *Thus is his cheek the map of days outworn,*
> *When **beauty** lived and died as flowers do now,*
> *Before these **bastard** signs of **fair** were born,*
> *Or durst inhabit on a living brow:*
> Sonnet 68, 1-4.

Taking *beauty* to be an allusion to the Queen (as confirmed by the balance of the sonnet and elsewhere), we deduce the result that *Sonnet 68* was written after her passing in 1603. Indeed, the transcendent "death sonnets", including *71, 73,* and *74,* augur Oxford's death in 1604. This take on *beauty* squares with an interesting passage found on page 58 of the novel:

> By this challenge I guess that either he was then in an ecstasy, or else sure I am now, in a **lunacy**, for it is a proud challenge made to **Beauty** herself and all her companions.

In particular, we note the play on the lunar Queen that the item *lunacy* evokes, with ***Beauty*** embedded into this picture of which she is an instantiation. The son is addressed as a Lord in *Sonnet 26,* consistent with his identification as the Earl of Southampton.

> ***Lord*** *of my love, to whom in vassalage*
> *Thy merit hath my duty strongly knit,*
> *To thee I send this written ambassage,*
> *To witness duty, not to show my wit.*
> Sonnet 26, 1-4.

Keeping in mind that Queen Elizabeth was renowned as the stellated queen, we turn to the third quatrain.

> *Till whatso**ever star** that guides my moving,*
> *Points on me graciously with **fair** aspect,*

And puts apparel on my tattered loving,
To show me worthy of their sweet respect.
Sonnet 26, 9-12.

The **star** that guided **E. Vere** was indeed the stellated monarch, and only she could determine his future moving, as revealed in the terminal couplet of this revelatory sonnet.

Then may I dare to boast how I do love thee;
Till then, not show my head where thou mayst prove me.
Sonnet 26, 13-4.

In other words, if and only if the Queen points on him with grace by recognizing his **fair aspect**, i.e. his Vere aspect, which is the son, will Oxford then dare to boast openly of his love for that son. With this analysis, we begin to understand the deeper meaning of the sonnets. Indeed, the significance of the son's identity is revealed by the terminal couplet of *Sonnet 70,* wherein the item *owe* is to be interpreted as *own* or *possess.*

If some suspect of ill masked not thy show,
*Then **thou alone kingdoms** of hearts shouldst owe.*
Sonnet 70, 13-4.

The reader will note that the fair youth is again identified with **alone,** another play on *tout par ung* along with its noted variant **all one.** And what was the suspect of ill by Southampton? A reasonable guess would be his participation in the Essex rebellion for which, curiously, there is no quick rational explanation for why he was not executed along with Essex and the other conspirators. The story of Southampton's imprisonment relates to *Sonnet 107,* even as some orthodox scholars have been willing to admit.

Not mine own fears, nor the prophetic soul
Of the wide world dreaming on things to come,
*Can yet the lease of **my true love** control,*
Supposed as forfeit to a confined doom.
Sonnet 107, 1-4.

Shakespeare-Oxford's true love was supposed as forfeit to a con-fined doom, an unmistakable allusion to Southampton's confine-ment in the Tower following on the Essex rebellion. The reader will now note that the Queen, this time in the guise of the mortal moon, is also mentioned.

> The **mortal moon** hath her eclipse endured,
> And the sad augurs mock their own presage,
> Incertainties now crown themselves assured,
> And peace proclaims olives of endless age.
> Sonnet 107, 5-8.

Confirming our claims most strongly is *Sonnet 134,* which we prefer to call the Tower sonnet.

> So now I have confessed that he is thine,
> And I myself am mortgaged to thy will,
> Myself I'll forfeit, so **that other mine**
> Thou wilt restore to be **my comfort still.**
> Sonnet 134, 1-4.

Some authors have seen in this a triangle of lovers, but it is clear that the phrase **that other mine** denotes the sonneteer's son consis-tent with **my comfort still,** none of which smacks of lovers' par-lance. In these lines the poet is pleading that the Queen "restore" his son by releasing him from the Tower. The plea fell on deaf ears as evidenced by the next quatrain, displaying another interesting oc-currence of the word *kind.*

> But thou wilt not, nor he will not be free,
> For thou art covetous, and he is kind;
> He learned but surety-like to write for me,
> Under that bond that him as fast doth bind.
> Sonnet 134, 5-8.

The terminal couplet of this same sonnet clinches our argument, as the author himself is not confined to the Tower, so that the fair youth truly "pays the whole" by imprisonment. The net result is that Shakespeare-Oxford suffers and hence is not free.

Him have I lost; thou hast both him and me.
He pays the whole, and yet am I not free.
                    Sonnet 134, 13-4.

It is obvious that there were powerful reasons behind Oxford's fixation on the Queen, as revealed throughout the sonnets and the plays under the *Shakespeare* pseudonym, and elsewhere under other pseudonyms. We suggest that some of these reasons had begun to crystallize as early as the 1570's. Ultimately the powerful research of Altrocchi [2002] on this topic must be carefully considered, to whose article we highly commend the reader.

True enough, the case for any one of the character identifications we have advanced above in connection with the novel is not half so clear as are the prototypes that Oxfordians have discovered in connection with the great plays, but whether or not any of the conjectures we have made in connection with the novel prove correct in the long run, what is crystal clear is that by recognizing Oxford as the author of *Flowers,* and hence of the Freeman Jones novel, we open up a rich store of questions for which answers appear more accessible than within the framework of orthodox criticism. In this spirit, we are able to reread the novel with far more interest and with a deeper understanding of its covert meaning. We gain thereby insight into how events and people in the author's life inspired him to write his novel in the first place we are thus treated to a novel penned by the very genius who later wrote under the pseudonym of *William Shakespeare.*

4. ELEMENTS OF EMPIRICAL CONFIRMATION

In this section we will amplify and elaborate on some of the evidence footnoted in our modern spelling edition. The sum of this elaboration will amount to more empirical confirmation of the claim that the Freeman Jones novel was written by the man who embraced the name *William Shakespeare,* that that man was indeed Edward de Vere, and that the character identifications suggested in the last section are sound. It is to be emphasized that these conclusions again show that the world's greatest literary genius was not the man from Stratford, but rather the noble de Vere.

FIRST ELEMENT OF EMPIRICAL CONFIRMATION:
pinching pain and *patience perforce*

Many orthodox scholars react to linguistic arguments about authorship in a manner reminiscent of Pavlov's dog. Thus, in response to Looney's original observation of the importance of the expression *pinching pain* for determining Shakespeare's true identity, some orthodox scholars have reacted by alleging that the expression is a commonplace and hence irrelevant to the authorship debate. Or consider our citation on page 112 establishing a linguistic relation between the passage in the novel and Oxford's verse with respect to the phrase *patience perforce*. To this some orthodox scholars would doubtless allege commonplace status to that phrase.

Just as these orthodox scholars conveniently fail to comment on the large numbers of congruences involving no conceivable commonplace material, so too they seem oblivious to the significance of commonplaces in the light of the cumulative effect of their presence within the relevant literature. Thus, status quo scholars also sow the seeds of their own destruction by failure to take into account what we have called convergence.

To bring the discussion to a head, we will again cite a crucial line from Oxford's poetry, this time emphasizing the convergence of *patience perforce* and the additional item *pinching pain* with two lines found in two stanzas of a single poem in the volume enclosing our novel. Indeed, we can provide a cascade from one poem in *Flowers* to de Vere's poem and back to another poem in *Flowers*.

FLOWERS: *Content thyself with **patience perforce**,*
                        ...
                *Believe me now it is a **pinching pain**,*

                        $\cong_{LEX-4}$
DE VERE: *Fain would I sing but fury makes me fret,*
                *And **rage** hath sworn to seek revenge of wrong;*
                ***My mazèd mind** in malice so is set*
                As death shall daunt my deadly dolors long.
                ***Patience perforce** is such a **pinching pain**,*
                As die I will or suffer wrong again.
                        May-10.

                        $\cong_{LEX-4}$
FLOWERS: *Such was the **rage**, that whilom did possess*
                *The privy corners of **my mazèd mind**:*

173

When hot desire did count those torments less
Which gained the gaze that did my freedom bind.

Such convergence of not one, but two so-called commonplace expressions, *patience perforce* and *pinching pain,* is not a consequence of commonplace availability per se. It is rather indicative of one and the same creator. This claim is confirmed by the addition of *rage* with *my mazèd mind* in such a way as to contribute to the same nexus of relations between de Vere's poem and poetry in *Flowers.*

To drive home the point, we might explore further the same poem by de Vere, where we find the expression *calm consent,* whence we note still more overlap with *Flowers,* including the noun *will.*

DE VERE:
> *I am no sot to suffer such abuse*
> *As doth bereave my heart of his delight,*
> *Nor will I frame myself to such as use*
> *With **calm consent** to suffer such despite.*
> > *No quiet sleep shall once possess mine eye,*
> > *Till wit have wrought **his will** on injury.*

≅*LEX-4*

FLOWERS:
> *And when he had with mickle pain procured*
> *The **calm consent** of **her** unwieldy **will**,*

So many convergent relations involving de Vere's poem can indicate one and one thing only and that is this, that one and only one mind was involved in the creation of it and of the poetry of *Flowers,* hence also of the associated novel. Now truth has a habit of revealing further truths. We witness as much when we append two more lines to the two lines cited from *Flowers* just above, whereupon we discern overlap with one of Shakespeare's *Will*-sonnets.

FLOWERS:
> *And when he had with mickle pain procured*
> *The calm consent of her unwieldy **will**,*
> *When he had her by faith and truth assured*
> *To like him best **and** ay to **love** him **still**,*

≅*LEX*, ≅*SYN*, ≅*RHYME*

SHAKESPEARE:
> *Make but my name thy love, **and love** that **still**,*
> *And then thou lovest me for my name is **Will**.*
> *Sonnet 136, 13-4.*

In this case impressive doses of lexical, syntactic, and rhyme congruences are manifest, just the kind of convergence one expects if the author of *Flowers* was indeed the man who later masked his identity behind the name *William Shakespeare.*

SECOND ELEMENT OF EMPIRICAL CONFIRMATION:
common vs. *enclosure*

A particularly striking example relating to our novelistic footnotes is witnessed in the following passage found on our page 39.

> The experiment she meant was this, for that she thought
> F.J.—I use her words—a man in every respect very worthy
> to have the *several* use of a more commodious *common*,
> she hoped now to see if his *enclosure* thereof might be
> defensible against her said secretary, and such like.

The author contrasts *several* with *common,* both being sixteenth century property terms meaning roughly 'private' and 'public', respectively. Of course, *enclosure* refers to enclosing land, thereby effectively privatizing it. The intended metaphor is that Elinor has been sexually receptive to others, i.e. common, but is now susceptible to enclosure by F.J. That enclosure, moreover, may not be defensible against Elinor's secretary.

The above passage borders on the stunning because Shakespeare uses the same metaphor in the third quatrain of *Sonnet 137,* which repeats the words *several* and *common* in a related context.

> *Why should my heart think that a **several** plot,*
> *Which my heart knows the wide world's **common** place?*
> *Or mine eyes, seeing this, say this is not*
> *To put **fair truth** upon so foul a face?*
> *Sonnet 137, 9-12.*

Although the word *several* and the phrase *fair truth* may involve plays on the author's family name Vere, it is the congruence of the two metaphors involving identical technical vocabulary that provides us with a new argument that we are truly dealing with one and the same author. In this connection our invitation to interpret Shakespeare's quatrain in a bawdy sense is confirmed by its preceding quatrain.

> *If eyes corrupt by over-partial looks*
> *Be anchored in the bay where all men ride,*
> *Why of eyes' falsehood hast thou forgèd hooks,*
> *Whereto the judgment of my heart is tied?*
> *Sonnet 137, 5-8.*

The "bay where all men ride" is a swipe at the dark lady and is obviously bawdy in its figurative content.

THIRD ELEMENT OF EMPIRICAL CONFIRMATION:
Theme of the torn letter, *descant, song,* and *burden.*

Turning to those events transpiring in the novel that have their counterparts in Shakespeare, we recall the episode of the torn letter in the novel, repeated in our modern spelling edition on page 8, where F.J. tears up what he believes to be his own letter. Thereupon he notices that it is in fact Elinor's letter, so he pieces the letter together and reads from the pieces.

With this episode from the novel the reader may compare a scene from Shakespeare's *Two Gentlemen of Verona.* Towards the beginning of that play, Julia tears up Proteus' letter and subsequently reads from the torn pieces. This action constitutes a significant point of convergence between novel and play, one indicative of a single author.

Two authors could have drawn on a similar idea. Therefore it is helpful to take cognizance of the attendant bawdy play found in the Shakespearean torn letter context.

Lucetta.	Ay, and melodious were it, would you sing it.
Julia.	And why not you?
Lucetta.	I cannot reach so high.
Julia.	Let's see your song. [*Takes the letter.*]
	How now, minion!
Lucetta.	Keep tune there still, so you will sing it out:
	And yet methinks I do not like this tune.
Julia.	You do not?
Lucetta.	No, madam; 'tis too sharp.
Julia.	You, minion, are too saucy.

176

Lucetta.   Nay, now you are too flat,
                And **mar** the concord with too harsh a **descant**.
                There wanteth but a **mean to fill your song**.
Julia.   The mean is drowned with your unruly bass.
Lucetta.   Indeed, I bid **the base** for Proteus.
Julia.   This babble shall not henceforth trouble me.
                Here is a coil with protestation!
                [*Tears the letter.*]
                Go get you gone, and let the papers lie;
                You would be fing'ring them, to anger me.

To those not invested in prudish readings of Shakespeare, it will be clear that the base is Proteus' penis and the song Julia's counterpart. Lucetta clearly plays with the word *descant,* noting that a mean is required to fill her mistress' song. The reader will recall a related constellation of references surrounding *descant* in the novel. Indeed, Lucetta's juxtaposition of the words *mar* and *descant* revisits a variation on these very words in the novelistic passage.

> And in very deed it fell out that the secretary, having been of long time absent and thereby his quills and pēnes not worn so near as they were wont to be, did now prick such fair large notes that his mistress liked better to sing faburden under him than to **descant** any longer upon F.J.'s plainsong. And thus they continued in good accord, until it fortuned that Dame Frances came into her chamber upon such sudden as she had like to have **marred** all the music.

The conjunction of torn letters, descants, and marrings argues that the two pieces, the novel on the one hand and the play on the other, are the creations of one and the same mind. And what may be even more cogently relevant vis-à-vis this last novelistic passage is its striking overlap with Shakespeare. Indeed, we witness the following impressively powerful cascade of bawdy fingerprints.

SHAKESPEARE:
> *Come **Philomel**, that sing'st of ravishment,*
> *Make thy sad grove in my disheveled hair;*
> *As the dank earth weeps at thy languishment,*
> *So I at each sad strain will strain a tear*
> *And with deep groans the diapason bear;*

> For **burden**-wise I'll hum on Tarquin still,
> While thou on Tereus **descants** better skill.
> The Rape of Lucrece, 1129-35.

FREEMAN:
> ... did now prick such fair large notes that his mistress liked better to sing **faburden** under him than to **descant** any longer upon F.J.'s **plainsong**.

SHAKESPEARE:
> Not that the summer is less pleasant now
> Than when her mournful hymns did hush the night,
> But that wild music **burdens** every bough,
> And sweets grown **common** lose their dear delight.
> Therefore, like her, I sometime hold my tongue,
> Because I would not dull you with my **song**.
> Sonnet 102, 9-14.

Note that Shakespeare employs the same bawdy figures in these pieces as does our anonymous novelist, a fact that cannot be explained under orthodox assumptions. Thus, in *Rape*, Shakespeare's **burden-wise** relates to the novel's **faburden**, with **descant** appearing in both, its attendant bawdy reading explained in our footnotes. Of course Tarquin and Tereus were both rapists and the bawdiness in Shakespeare's narrative poems is evident from his overt use of the word *ravishment*. The sonnet is subtle, however, and no one seems to make the relevant connection, in spite of the fact that our previously noted bawdy item **common** makes an appearance. The bawdy is easily grasped, however, once **Philomel** in *Rape* is noted along with its related presence in the middle quatrain of the sonnet.

> Our love was new, and then but in the spring,
> When I was wont to greet it with **my lays**,
> As **Philomel** in summer's front doth sing,
> And stops her pipe in growth of riper days.
> Sonnet 102, 5-8.

Of course **my lays** also invites the same kind of bawdy reading that we encounter many times in the novel. As for the item **descant**, evidence from another source supports our claim to the author's bawdy intent of this word denoting a tune or melody sung above a musical theme.

> *Come sing with me, and if these notes be low,*
> *You shall have some pricked higher ere ye go.*
> *Cephalis and Procris*

This couplet mirrors our novelist's interest in playing on higher notes via *descant*, as also Shakespeare's, suggesting that we consider the name associated with the last couplet, namely *Thomas Edwards,* another pseudonym for the author of the novel, namely Edward de Vere. This last claim is empirically confirmed in *Never and For Ever*. Even here the resonant reader will recognize the affinity of the above couplet with one Shakespeare provides in *Venus and Adonis,* supporting our claim.

> *Graze on **my lips, and if those** hills be dry,*
> *Stray lower, where the pleasant fountains lie.*
> *Venus and Adonis, 233-4.*
>
> ≅*LEX-5,* ≅*SYN*
> *Come sing with **me, and if these** notes be low,*
> *You shall have some pricked higher ere ye go.*
> *Cephalis and Procris*

Surely the syntactic relatedness of the two couplets smacks of one mind, but the lexical overlap is equally revealing, all the more so in view of the fact that both are erotically framed in the deviously clever manner we know to be Shakespeare's.

FOURTH ELEMENT OF EMPIRICAL CONFIRMATION:
bottoms and *silks*

Still another area of overlap concerns the author's use of the word *bottom,* most relevantly as introduced in one of F.J.'s letters.

> And let this poor paper, besprent with salt tears and blown over with scalding sighs, be saved of you as a safeguard for your sampler, or a **bottom** to **wind** your sewing **silk**, that when your last needle full is wrought, you may return to reading thereof and consider the care of him who is
> *More yours than his own.*
> *F.J.*

The conjunction of the words *bottom* and *silk,* and as we will eventually find, also *wind,* is of interest for the convergence of three separate strands of evidence establishing Oxford's authorship.

The *bottom/silk* motif surely relates to Nick Bottom, the weaver, the assified mechanical of the great fairy play *A Midsummer Night's Dream.* Apprised of the fact that the word *bottom* is a term for spool or winding instrument for thread, but also for the silk cocoon, we recognize the connection with the fact that Bottom's profession is that of a silk weaver.

Among the arguments suggesting that Bottom is to be identified with Oxford are these: (*i*) Oxford often splits in his dramatic creations to assume the role of both protagonist of the play and its butt, be the latter clown, jester, or fool, thereby giving insight into both his noble self and his comedic persona. In the fairy play, the noble self is revealed in Oberon, the butt in Bottom; (*ii*) a striking proportional analogy with the novel emerges by recognizing Bottom as modeled on Oxford: F.J. is to Elinor as Bottom is to Titania. It is summarized in the following proportional relation:

$$\text{F.J.}\,/\,\text{ELINOR} \equiv \text{BOTTOM}\,/\,\text{TITANIA}$$

The analogy is well motivated in view of the fact that Bottom sleeps with Titania in the play as does F.J. with Elinor in the novel. A potent clue to Shakespeare's deeper meaning is that the name *Titania* is an Ovidian variant of *Diana.* Thus, there is reason to believe that the Queen of the fairies is modeled on Queen Elizabeth and hence the Bottom-Titania connection provides a link to the Freeman Jones novel under Dickinson's conjecture. Finally, (*iii*) Bottom plays Pyramus in the play-within-the-play. Of the fact that he must draw his sword before "the ladies", he makes much ado, in fact too large a point not to involve a deeper secret.

Bottom: ... tell them that I Pyramus am not Pyramus, but Bottom the weaver. This will put them out of fear.

Clearly Bottom is overly zealous to reveal that he is a weaver. This otherwise strange behavior is explained if he is in fact identifying himself as the hidden author. That is, the word *weaver* is a straightforward play on **E. Vere**. That *ver*-play is indeed involved is further suggested by Quince's overwrought emphasis on Pyramus' cue, as revealingly confirmed by Thisbe.

Quince. Your cue is past; it is "**never** tire."
Thisbe. **O**, as **true** as truest horse that yet would **never** tire.
Pyramus. If **I were fair**, Thisbe, I were only thine.
Quince. **O** monstrous! **O** strange!

The emphasis on Pyramus' cue words, i.e. Bottom's, is a subtle clue that Bottom is Ne(d) Vere. There follows a wealth of additional wordplay items relating to Vere and Oxford. To further confirm our claims, we note that Bottom is addressed by Quince: "What sayest thou, bully Bottom?"

But why bully? Plausibly, it is because the play's weaver was in a real sense modeled on an ox, namely on **Ox**ford.

FIFTH ELEMENT OF EMPIRICAL CONFIRMATION: Pyramus-Thisbe Legend

An amazing convergence of the Pyramus-Thisbe legend with the *silk-bottom* motif, including the idea of winding, is found in a lovely poem associated with the author's *T. M.* pseudonym. It is entitled *The Silkewormes, and their Flies* and was published in 1599. Two of its stanzas attest that a bottom is a silk cocoon, for which we will here cite only one.

> *Yet that there might remain some **Pyramis**,*
> *And everlasting shrine of Pyram's love,*
> *When leaves are gone and summer waning is,*
> *The little creepers never cease to move,*
> *But day and night, placing in toil their bliss,*
> *Spin **silk** this tree beneath and eke above,*
> > *Leaving their oval **bottoms** there behind,*
> > *To show the state of ev'ry lover's mind.*

It may well be that *ev'ry lover's* is intended to highlight E. Vere's mind. At any rate, the convergence with winding emerges two stanzas later by way of analogy between silk cocoons as hearses for the silkworm and shrouds.

> *That still we make our love our **winding** sheet,*
> *Whilst more we love, or hotter than is meet.*

In *Never and For Ever* we show that T. M. is indeed Oxford, which yields another link to Shakespeare via the convergence with *A Midsummer Night's Dream*. It is interesting to note that some orthodox scholars have viewed T.M.'s poem as a source for Shakespeare's play, while others deny any such influence. If we are right, there was no influence per se, just one author's mind being reflected in two distinct contexts. Thus, those who claim the poem as a source are wrong to do so, but are to be commended nonetheless for perceiving its Shakespearean relatedness. That relatedness is no accident in view of the all too obvious *Pyramus-silk-bottom-wind* concept cluster. By contrast, those who fail to perceive any significant relatedness between the silkworm poem and the fairy play, most famously former Harvard professor Douglas Bush, as quoted by Houliston [1989] in the introduction to his facsimile reprint, are to be discommended, even if they are technically correct about sources per se. Our belief is that anyone failing to perceive that the silkworm poem was penned by the author of *Venus and Adonis*, suffused as it is with such radiant beauty and genius, is likely to be incapable of resonating with Shakespeare in other ways. Is it any wonder that orthodox critics are unable to recognize Shakespeare's true identity and with it his work as a novelist?

The *bottom* terminology is encountered in yet another poem with demonstrable links to Vere. The source we give below; for now we note that the following couplet relates to the novel by way of connecting bottoms, silks, letters, and winding.

*A **bottom** for your **silk** it seems my **letters** have become,*
*Which with oft **winding** off and on are wasted whole and some.*

The winding may well evoke a double entendre, suggested perhaps by the conjunction of *off* and *on,* but we are content here only to note the identical deployment by the author of the novelistic letter as a bottom for winding silk (cf. bottom of page 179), from which it is reasonable to conclude that the author is addressing in the poem the very same mistress denoted by *Elinor* in the novel. Continuing, we have:

*Who nilling other for to find but through **my** painting **pen**,*
Thereto to give occasion to write you will not len,
*And sith you take such great delight **my bottoms** for to spend,*
Behold now granting to your will, another here I find.

The author speaks of his pen, again a plausible penile reference, and grants to his former mistress' will another bottom or letter to serve as an instrument for winding silk. And several lines later:

'Tis seldom seen a swan to dive, of more hens had been best
For you to talk, although you seem that name for to detest.
***Diana's troop** is best may blaze the swan of Menander,*
It best becomes your pen to paint the goose and the gander.

Diana is again brought into the exposition, and we must admit that the name would have been recognized by all educated Elizabethans as quite plausibly denoting the Queen. In the next lines the clearest of clues surfaces to establish the author of the poetry as Vere.

Whose tongue doth run before your wit,
                    and shows fools' bolts soon shot:
*You would a good Virgilian be, if **Vir** in place were not.*

Another reference to Diana, hence Elizabeth, is found in the next few lines.

Sometime if Ovid took delight to praise the hazel nut,
If Virgil vaunting of his gnat, why do not I forth put
Myself to paint thy juggling tricks? Secluding dalliance,
Who knows so well my legerdemains with false conveyance.
You are Medusa, that fiend-like mare, no more a courtesan,
*You are no more a soaring hawk, what then a chaste **Diane**?*

This revealing poem is entitled *Grange's Garden* and its alleged author, John Grange, is Oxford, a claim we have endeavored to verified in *Never and For Ever* during the course of our exploration of Shakespeare as a novelist.

SIXTH ELEMENT OF EMPIRICAL CONFIRMATION:
Ver-play

We have repeatedly observed that the modern mind is predisposed to be unreceptive to wordplay. In this connection, it is worthwhile recalling that throughout the Renaissance, censorship was rife and that authors consequently utilized wordplay to hint at what might otherwise be censored. The novel provided here yields a wealth of potential examples involving *ver*-play, many of which we have not marked in our notes. For example, on page 5 the narrator speaks of the author: *Until it be finished you may guess him by his Nature.* Not implausibly, the author is here playing on his name via *Nat-ure* ≡ *Ned Ver*, very much as Shakespeare covertly intends *Adonis* in his great narrative poem *Venus and Adonis* to be interpreted by the brighter sort as *Ad-o* ≡ *Ed O*, i.e. Ed Oxford.

We also wish to emphasize that the balance of the *Flowers* volume within which the Freeman Jones novel is ensconced contains a wealth of wordplay instances confirming Oxford's authorship. Apart from a poem recognized as referring to de Vere by the orthodox Pigman [2000] and analyzed in detail in *Never and For Ever*, many more poems include wordplay on the author's family name *Vere,* including those with signature byline *Ever or Never.* The word *Ever* relates to Shakespeare's *Sonnet 76* and *Sonnet 105,* as discussed earlier, while *Never* is a plausible play on the name *Ned Vere,* the first name being a well-attested nick-name for *Edward,* the author's first name.

As for the novel's Elinor, her name remains in the revision, but is metamorphosed to *Leonora* in its introduction without loss of covert information provided one admits wordplay indicated by the word's formal segmentation as *Leon-ora,* with *Leon* standing for 'lion' and *ora* for 'golden', hence the Queen, whose lion is seen in two quarters of her coat of arms that we have provided above on page 145. This naturally returns us to the name *Elinor* whose analysis may be *El-in-or,* i.e. 'El in gold'. The author's fixation on the Queen recalls Talbot's letter cited above relating to "love matters". In a related vein, Nicolas [1847: 15] claims that Mary Queen of Scots said that "the Earl of Oxford dared not cohabit with his wife" for the reason given in the following extract of Mary's letter in French, which translates:

> out of fear of losing the favor which he hoped to receive
> by making love to you

The crowning covert reading of the original name *Freeman Iones,* might therefore be this: *Vere man, I(am)one's,* in which case it would be better to forego *F.J.* and retain *F.I.* as itself.

APPENDIX 1: *Margination*

Throughout our modern spelling edition of the Freeman Jones novel, we have drawn on the device of daggered footnotes to indicate potential plays on the author's name *E. Vere* and on his title, *Earl of Oxford.* Many wordplay items might not have been recognizable as such were it not for additional authorial clues or aids to their decipherment as purposefully left behind by the author. One such aid is what we term *margination,* by which we recognize that de Vere chose to align wordplay items with a margin of a page to make recognition of his hand discernible. Such alignment indicates that Oxford was intimately associated with his publisher and may well have subsidized this and other of his creations, which may in turn have contributed to his eventual financial straits. Moreover we

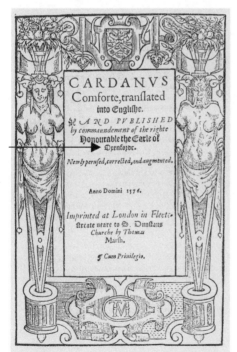

will discover the astonishing fact that he employed the same device over his own signature.

A special case of margination is that witnessed on title pages. An overt instance of this type is found on the title page of the translation *Cardanus Comforte,* a book that we referred to earlier in connection with *Flowers* and also with Pettie.

Notice the word *Oxenforde* displayed on the title page as an item of both left and right margination whose presence we signal with our interpolated arrow. Stretching the definition, we might also take the word *Earle* on this page to be a case of margination, as it is separated from the right margin by only the short word *of,* which is part of de Vere's title. These examples are ones we choose to characterize as *overt margination,* since the denotation of *Oxen-*

forde is overtly given for all to recognize. In other words, nothing is hidden.

By striking contrast, we encounter a second example when we turn to the book within which our novel is situated, whose title page frames a remarkable case of *covert margination*.

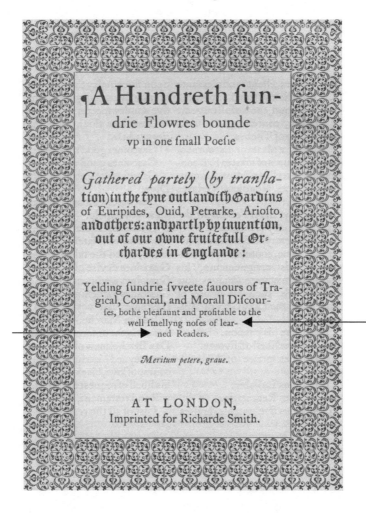

Inspecting this facsimile title page, we see that the works found in *Flowers* are *pleasant and profitable to the Vere smelling noses of Earl Ned's readers,* where one obtains *earl* by permutation of the letter in *lear* with the following three. In particular, they are profitable to the *well* smelling nose, with *well* providing a potential example of *el*-play. Thus, both margins are utilized on the title page as an aid to determining Oxford's identity as author of the volume with a more arcane clue possibly divulging his regal target.

Margination subsumes sidenotes and catchwords as special cases, along with another particular case of paramount importance, one we have chosen to call *hyphenation*. A striking example of this type of margination is evident on the title page of our preceding example, as witnessed in the hyphenated item *lear-*. It is to be noted that hyphenation yields an additional clue, over and beyond simple margination, to the effect that the author is playing on his noble title. Even so, this example would not be entirely convincing were it not for the cumulative effect of margination that we find in the book (and in others, as we show in *Never and For Ever*).

For background, note that a potential text-embedded example of margination is found on the first page of the letter signed E. of Oxenford as published in the *Cardanus* volume. A facsimile reproduction of the relevant part of this page is provided below with our arrows added to indicate the relevant margination items.

Fter I had perufed youre letters good mayfter Bedingfeld, findinge in thē your requeftfarre differinge from the defert of your labour, I could not chofe but gretly doubte, whether it were better for mee to yelde you youre defire, or execute myne owne intention towardes the publifhinge of your Booke. For I do confeffe the affections that I haue alwayes borne towardes you coulde moue mee not a lyttle. But when I had throughly confidered in my minde of fondrye and di- ◄ uers argumentes, whether it were beft to obeye myne affec- ► ticns or the merites of your ftudyes: At the length I determined it better to denye your vnlawfull requeft, then to graunt or condifcende to the concealement of fo worthy a

We have here a typical example of right hyphenation intended to relate *di/uers argumentes* in the minds of knowledgeable readers to *de Vere's arguments*. Hyphenation is covert in the sense that not all readers are able to grasp the hidden pun. (The item *deter-* two lines below may also constitute such an example, inasmuch as the hyphen draws special attention to the sequence, which approximates the sequence *de Ver*.)

This is the kind of meaningful hyphenation that we find throughout *Flowers*. That it is cumulative suggests that Oxford played incessantly on his family name and noble title. An excerpt from the first edition provides an illustrative example drawn from page 244 of that original.

and thereuppon grew a great quarrell. When thefe ver- ⬅
fes were by the negligence of his Miftreffe difperfed in
to fundzy hands, and fo at laft to the reading of a Courtier. Well F. I. had his defire ifhis Miftreffe lyked them,
but as I haue heard him declare, fhe grew in icolofic, that
the fame were not written by hir, becaufe hir name was
Elynor and not *Hellen*. And about this poynt haue bene
➡ diuers and fundzy opinions, for this and diuers other of
his moft notable Poems, haue come to biew of y wozld,

In this excerpt we have one right hyphenation item *ver-* and a left margination item *diuers* reminiscent of the previous example found in Oxford's letter. We also witness an interlinear occurrence of *divers* within the same line. Another illustration is found on the opening page of H.W.'s introductory message to readers of the novel, which we provide in full on the next page. (Note that 'y^e' early in the page is to be understood as an abbreviation of the definite article *the*.) At the margins of this page we meet with two important items that we have singled out with arrows, both redolent of Oxfordian wordplay, as clarified in the following annotated tabular display.

ITEM	RIGHT MARGIN	LEFT MARGIN	PUN
verses		*verses*	*Vere*
redelive/red	*redelive-*	*red*	*Ed, de Vere, Ed*

We would be unimpressed with such examples were it not that a wealth of potential wordplay material is scattered across the page, including another instance of *divers* in line 6, *deliver* in line 13, *learned Reader* in line 21, as well as *Lover* in line 25. (Words such as *adventured* and *devises* may also be intended as puns.) All such nonmarginal items are summarized in the following table.

A diſcourſe of the aduentures   **201**

paſſed by Maſter F. I.

H. VV. to the Reader.

N Auguſt laſt paſſed my familiar friend Maſter G. T. beſtowed vppon me ý reading of a wzit-ten Booke, wherin he had collected diuers diſcourſes & verſes, inuented vppon ſun-dzie occaſions , by ſundzie gentlemē(in mine opinion) right commendable foz their capacitie. And herewithal my ſaid friend charged me, that I ſhould vſe them onely foz mine owne particuler com-moditie, and eftſones ſafely deliuer the ozignall copie to him againe, wherein I muſt confeſſe my ſelfe but halfe a marchant, foz the copie vnto him I haue ſafely redeliue-red. But the wozke(foz I thought it wozthy to be publi-liſhed)I haue entreated my friend A.B. to empzint: as one that thought better to pleaſe a number by common commoditie then to feede the humoz of any pziuate parſon by nedeleſſe ſingularitie. This I haue aduentured, foz thy contentation(learned Reader.)And further haue pze-ſumed of my ſelfe to chziſten it by the name of A hundreth ſundrie Flowers : In which poeticall poſie are ſetfozth ma-nie trifling fantaſies, humozall paſſions, and ſtraunge af-fects of a Louer. And therin(although the wiſer ſozt wold turne ouer the leafe as a thing altogether fruitleſſe)yet I my ſelfe haue reaped this commoditie, to ſit and ſmile at the fond deuiſes of ſuch as haue enchayned them ſelues in the golden fetters of fantaſie, and hauing betwzayed them

A.i.   ſelues

INTERLINEAR WORDPLAY ITEMS	
ITEM	PUN
divers	*de Vere's*
deliver	*de Vere*
learned Reader	*Earl Ned Reader*
Lover	*Oxford Vere*

Note that the author—billed as H.W.—is introducing and commending **divers** discourses and **verses**; hence we may take the word *divers* to be interpretable as *de Vere's* and *verses* to be a plausible play on the author's family name *Vere*. Additional pages in the original copy are also revealing.

Admittedly, wordplay can be a slippery topic and we must resist the temptation of attributing it to passages where it was never intended by the author. There are further reasons, however, that convince us we are not recording ghosts of departing quantities. In the first place, we find a remarkable accumulation of potential margination items on specific pages of the novel. This we call *local accumulation*. Consider in this respect the margination items on the novel's original page 246, with a summary of *ver*-play provided in the table immediately below along with an added indication of original hyphens.

ITEM	RIGHT MARGIN	LEFT MARGIN	PUN
ve-ry	*ve-*	*ry*	*Vere*
Lovers	*Lovers*		*Oxford Vere*
ve-ry	*ve-*	*ry*	*Vere*
verse		*verse*	*Vere*

A second point is this: when one keys in the pages bearing the accumulated margination items into a digital computer using a word processing program, one commonly loses the accumulation of margination *ver*-play found on such pages of *Flowers*. To wit, let us compare the last page of examples involving six margination items with the repaginated edition found in Pigman [2000: 178]. Pigman's edition effectively destroys all six items save one, the left margination item *verse*. With all due respect to his scholarship, we thus find that Pigman's edition involves a significant loss of potential wordplay information, this being a consequence of his failure to recognize the author of *Flowers* as Edward de Vere.

A third reason for believing that we are not chasing a will-of-the-wisp has to do with what we may call *global accumulation*. Thus, one finds *ver*-play stretching across many pages of *Flowers,* from which we have drawn on three such pages in this section. Crucially, we meet with revealing margination in a number of de Vere's literary creations and letters, associated both with his signature and with pseudonyms, many examples of which are adduced and discussed in *Never and For Ever.* This we take to be our fourth and most powerful point.

Indeed, Oxford employed hyphenation over his own signature in a most subtle manner, as we witness in an excerpt from his letter in *Cardanus Comforte,* a facsimile exhibited here with arrows to mark Oxford's deployment of hyphenation in two distinct cases. Note how our author attributes to his friend his own shadow with a revealing phrase "a

bes : VVhereby when they be deade in deede, yet make we them liue as it were againe through theyr monument, but wyth me behold it happeneth farre better, for in your lyfe time I shall erect you such a monumet, that as I saye youre life time you shall see howe noble a shadowe of youre ver- ◀— tuous life, shall hereafter remaine when you are deade and gone. And in your life time againe I say, I shall giue you that monunient and remembraunce of your life, whereby I may declare my good will though: vvith your ill will as yet that I do beare you in youre life . Thus earnestly de- fyringe you in this on: requeft of mine (as I woulde yelde to you in a great m iny) not to repugne the fettinge forth of your owne prop:r ftudies, I bid you farewell.

¶ From my new countrep Males at VViuengho!e, wy- ◀— shing you as you haue begunne, to proceede in thefe ver- tuous actions. For when all things shall els forfake vs, vertue yet will euer abide with vs, and when our bodies falles into the bowels of the earth, yet that shall mounte with our minnes into the highest Heauens,

By youre louinge and affured
frende. E. Oxenford.

shadowe of youre ver-", essentially admitting to his authorship of the *Cardanus* translation. In this letter, Oxford deploys still more margination wordplay, which we discuss at length in *Never and For Ever*, the second installment of our fingerprint trilogy.

A fifth point recalls the most obvious species of *ver*-play in conjunction with multiple identifications of F.J. as E. Vere, including such phrases as *very good friend F.J., even so F.J. (my friend F.J.), ever he*, and the like, along with the *Ever or Never* byline associated with some of the poetry of *Flowers*. Here it is significant that we find a related pun on the name *E. Vere* in the Bedingfeld letter to Oxford found in *Cardanus Comforte*.

TO THE RIGHTE
Honourable and my good Lord
the Earle of Oxenforde, Lorde great
Chamberlayne of Englande.

Y GOOD LORDE, I can geene nothinge more agreable to your minde, and my fortune then the willinge performance of futch feruice as it fhall pleafe you to cõmaunde me vnto: And therefore rather to obeye then boaft of my cunninge, and as a newe figne of myne olde deuotion, I doe prefent the booke your Lordefhip fo longe defired. VVith affured hope that how *fo euer you* miflike or allow ther of, you will fauourably conceale myne imperfeĉtions

In particular, note that Oxford is addressed in the second to last line of the display with the words *so ever you*, which we have underscored for ease of reference in our facsimile reproduction. The pun here is another instance of the type we have claimed for the novel throughout the footnotes. Of course here it is more immediately accessible, since E. Vere's identity is not covert, the letter's heading clearly identifying the Earl of Oxford.

Although neither of your editors is young enough to know everything, we offer a final point to illustrate that we do know something and that is the relevant point that an author can have sufficient control over his publisher and/or printer as to insure margination where appropriate. Thus, the astute reader will have recognized our own